IN ASSOCIATION WITH

✗ SQA

Hodder Gibson
Model Practice
Papers
WITH ANSWERS

PLUS: Official SQA Specimen Paper With Answers

Higher for CfE

Mathematics

2014 Specimen Question Paper & Model Papers

HODDER
GIBSON
AN HACHETTE UK COMPANY

This book contains the official 2014 SQA Specimen Question Paper for Higher for CfE Maths, with associated SQA approved answers modified from the official marking instructions that accompany the paper.

In addition the book contains model practice papers, together with answers, plus study skills advice. These papers, some of which may include a limited number of previously published SQA questions, have been specially commissioned by Hodder Gibson, and have been written by experienced senior teachers and examiners in line with the new Higher for CfE syllabus and assessment outlines, Spring 2014. This is not SQA material but has been devised to provide further practice for Higher for CfE examinations in 2014 and beyond.

Hodder Gibson is grateful to the copyright holders, as credited on the final page of the Answer Section, for permission to use their material. Every effort has been made to trace the copyright holders and to obtain their permission for the use of copyright material. Hodder Gibson will be happy to receive information allowing us to rectify any error or omission in future editions.

Hachette UK's policy is to use papers that are natural, renewable and recyclable products and made from wood grown in sustainable forests. The logging and manufacturing processes are expected to conform to the environmental regulations of the country of origin.

Orders: please contact Bookpoint Ltd, 130 Park Drive, Abingdon, Oxon OX14 4SE. Telephone: (44) 01235 827720. Fax: (44) 01235 400454. Lines are open 9.00–5.00, Monday to Saturday, with a 24-hour message answering service. Visit our website at www.hoddereducation.co.uk. Hodder Gibson can be contacted direct on: Tel: 0141 848 1609; Fax: 0141 889 6315; email: hoddergibson@hodder.co.uk

This collection first published in 2014 by
Hodder Gibson, an imprint of Hodder Education,
An Hachette UK Company
2a Christie Street
Paisley PA1 1NB

{BrightRED   Hodder Gibson is grateful to Bright Red Publishing Ltd for collaborative work in preparation of this book and all SQA Past Paper, National 5 and Higher for CfE Model Paper titles 2014.

Typeset by PDQ Digital Media Solutions Ltd, Bungay, Suffolk NR35 1BY

Printed in the UK

A catalogue record for this title is available from the British Library

ISBN: 978-1-4718-3723-4

3 2 1

2015 2014

Introduction

Study Skills – what you need to know to pass exams!

Pause for thought

Many students might skip quickly through a page like this. After all, we all know how to revise. Do you really though?

Think about this:

"IF YOU ALWAYS DO WHAT YOU ALWAYS DO, YOU WILL ALWAYS GET WHAT YOU HAVE ALWAYS GOT."

Do you like the grades you get? Do you want to do better? If you get full marks in your assessment, then that's great! Change nothing! This section is just to help you get that little bit better than you already are.

There are two main parts to the advice on offer here. The first part highlights fairly obvious things but which are also very important. The second part makes suggestions about revision that you might not have thought about but which WILL help you.

Part 1

DOH! It's so obvious but …

Start revising in good time

Don't leave it until the last minute – this will make you panic.

Make a revision timetable that sets out work time AND play time.

Sleep and eat!

Obvious really, and very helpful. Avoid arguments or stressful things too – even games that wind you up. You need to be fit, awake and focused!

Know your place!

Make sure you know exactly **WHEN and WHERE** your exams are.

Know your enemy!

Make sure you know what to expect in the exam.

How is the paper structured?

How much time is there for each question?

What types of question are involved?

Which topics seem to come up time and time again?

Which topics are your strongest and which are your weakest?

Are all topics compulsory or are there choices?

Learn by DOING!

There is no substitute for past papers and practice papers – they are simply essential! Tackling this collection of papers and answers is exactly the right thing to be doing as your exams approach.

Part 2

People learn in different ways. Some like low light, some bright. Some like early morning, some like evening / night. Some prefer warm, some prefer cold. But everyone uses their BRAIN and the brain works when it is active. Passive learning – sitting gazing at notes – is the most INEFFICIENT way to learn anything. Below you will find tips and ideas for making your revision more effective and maybe even more enjoyable. What follows gets your brain active, and active learning works!

Activity 1 – Stop and review

Step 1

When you have done no more than 5 minutes of revision reading STOP!

Step 2

Write a heading in your own words which sums up the topic you have been revising.

Step 3

Write a summary of what you have revised in no more than two sentences. Don't fool yourself by saying, "I know it, but I cannot put it into words". That just means you don't know it well enough. If you cannot write your summary, revise that section again, knowing that you must write a summary at the end of it. Many of you will have notebooks full of blue/black ink writing. Many of the pages will not be especially attractive or memorable so try to liven them up a bit with colour as you are reviewing and rewriting. **This is a great memory aid, and memory is the most important thing.**

Activity 2 — Use technology!

Why should everything be written down? Have you thought about "mental" maps, diagrams, cartoons and colour to help you learn? And rather than write down notes, why not record your revision material?

What about having a text message revision session with friends? Keep in touch with them to find out how and what they are revising and share ideas and questions.

Why not make a video diary where you tell the camera what you are doing, what you think you have learned and what you still have to do? No one has to see or hear it, but the process of having to organise your thoughts in a formal way to explain something is a very important learning practice.

Be sure to make use of electronic files. You could begin to summarise your class notes. Your typing might be slow, but it will get faster and the typed notes will be easier to read than the scribbles in your class notes. Try to add different fonts and colours to make your work stand out. You can easily Google relevant pictures, cartoons and diagrams which you can copy and paste to make your work more attractive and **MEMORABLE**.

Activity 3 – This is it. Do this and you will know lots!

Step 1

In this task you must be very honest with yourself! Find the SQA syllabus for your subject (www.sqa.org.uk). Look at how it is broken down into main topics called MANDATORY knowledge. That means stuff you MUST know.

Step 2

BEFORE you do ANY revision on this topic, write a list of everything that you already know about the subject. It might be quite a long list but you only need to write it once. It shows you all the information that is already in your long-term memory so you know what parts you do not need to revise!

Step 3

Pick a chapter or section from your book or revision notes. Choose a fairly large section or a whole chapter to get the most out of this activity.

With a buddy, use Skype, Facetime, Twitter or any other communication you have, to play the game "If this is the answer, what is the question?". For example, if you are revising Geography and the answer you provide is "meander", your buddy would have to make up a question like "What is the word that describes a feature of a river where it flows slowly and bends often from side to side?".

Make up 10 "answers" based on the content of the chapter or section you are using. Give this to your buddy to solve while you solve theirs.

Step 4

Construct a wordsearch of at least 10 X 10 squares. You can make it as big as you like but keep it realistic. Work together with a group of friends. Many apps allow you to make wordsearch puzzles online. The words and phrases can go in any direction and phrases can be split. Your puzzle must only contain facts linked to the topic you are revising. Your task is to find 10 bits of information to hide in your puzzle, but you must not repeat information that you used in Step 3. DO NOT show where the words are. Fill up empty squares with random letters. Remember to keep a note of where your answers are hidden but do not show your friends. When you have a complete puzzle, exchange it with a friend to solve each other's puzzle.

Step 5

Now make up 10 questions (not "answers" this time) based on the same chapter used in the previous two tasks. Again, you must find NEW information that you have not yet used. Now it's getting hard to find that new information! Again, give your questions to a friend to answer.

Step 6

As you have been doing the puzzles, your brain has been actively searching for new information. Now write a NEW LIST that contains only the new information you have discovered when doing the puzzles. Your new list is the one to look at repeatedly for short bursts over the next few days. Try to remember more and more of it without looking at it. After a few days, you should be able to add words from your second list to your first list as you increase the information in your long-term memory.

FINALLY! Be inspired...

Make a list of different revision ideas and beside each one write **THINGS I HAVE** tried, **THINGS I WILL** try and **THINGS I MIGHT** try. Don't be scared of trying something new.

And remember – "FAIL TO PREPARE AND PREPARE TO FAIL!"

Higher Mathematics

The course

The Higher Mathematics course aims to:

- motivate and challenge learners by enabling them to select and apply mathematical techniques in a variety of mathematical situations

- develop confidence in the subject and a positive attitude towards further study in mathematics and the use of mathematics in employment

- deliver in-depth study of mathematical concepts and the ways in which mathematics describes our world

- allow learners to interpret, communicate and manage information in mathematical form; skills which are vital to scientific and technological research and development

- deepen learners' skills in using mathematical language and exploring advanced mathematical ideas.

The Higher qualification in Mathematics is designed to build upon and extend learners' mathematical skills, knowledge and understanding in a way that recognises problem solving as an essential skill and enables them to integrate their knowledge of different aspects of the subject.

You will acquire an enhanced awareness of the importance of mathematics to technology and to society in general. Where appropriate, mathematics will be developed in context, and mathematical techniques will be applied in social and vocational contexts related to likely progression routes such as commerce, engineering and science where the mathematics learned will be put to direct use.

The syllabus is designed to build upon your prior learning in the areas of algebra, geometry and trigonometry and to introduce you to elementary calculus.

How the course is assessed

- To gain the Course award, you must pass the three units – Expressions & Functions, Relationships & Calculus, and Applications - as well as the examination.

- The units are assessed internally on a pass/fail basis.

- The examination is set and marked by the SQA.

- The course award is graded A–D, the grade being determined by the total mark you score in the examination.

The examination

- The examination consists of two papers. The number of marks and the times allotted for the papers are:

  Paper 1
  (non-calculator) 60 marks 1 hour 10 minutes
  Paper 2   70 marks 1 hour 30 minutes

- The examination tests skills beyond the minimum competence required for the units. Both papers contain short and extended response questions in which candidates are required to apply numerical, algebraic, geometric, trigonometric, calculus, and reasoning skills.

- The examination is designed so that approximately 65% of the marks will be available for level C responses.

- Some questions will assess only operational skills (65% of the marks) but other questions will require both operational and reasoning skills (35% of the marks).

Further details can be found in the Higher Mathematics section on the SQA website: http://www.sqa.org.uk/sqa/47910.html.

Key tips for your success

Practise! Practise! Practise!

DOING maths questions is the most effective use of your study time. You will benefit much more from spending 30 minutes doing maths questions than spending several hours copying out notes or reading a maths textbook.

Basic skills

You must practise the following essential basic skills for Higher Mathematics throughout the duration of this course - expanding brackets; solving equations; manipulating algebraic expressions; and, in particular, working with exact values with trigonometric expressions and equations.

Non-routine problems

It is important to practise non-routine problems as often as possible throughout the course, particularly if you are aiming for an A or B pass in Higher Mathematics.

Graph sketching

Graph sketching is an important and integral part of Mathematics. Ensure that you practise sketching graphs on plain paper whenever possible throughout this course. Neither squared nor graph paper are allowed in the Higher Mathematics examination.

Marking instructions

Ensure that you look at the detailed marking instructions of past papers. They provide further advice and guidelines as well as showing you precisely where, and for what, marks are awarded.

Show all working clearly

The instructions on the front of the exam paper state that *"Full credit will be given only where the solution contains appropriate working."* A "correct" answer with no working may only be awarded partial marks or even no marks at all. An incomplete answer will be awarded marks for any appropriate working. Attempt every question, even if you are not sure whether you are correct or not. Your solution may contain working which will gain some marks. A blank response is certain to be awarded no marks. Never score out working unless you have something better to replace it with.

Make drawings

Try drawing what you visualise as the "picture", described within the wording of each relevant question. This is a mathematical skill expected of most candidates at Higher level. Making a rough sketch of the diagram in your answer booklet may also help you interpret the question and achieve more marks.

Extended response questions

You should look for connections between parts of questions, particularly where there are three or four sections to a question. These are almost always linked and, in some instances, an earlier result in part (a) or (b) is needed and its use would avoid further repeated work.

Notation

In all questions, make sure that you use the correct notation. In particular, for integration questions, remember to include '*dx*' within your integral.

Radians

Remember to work in radians when attempting any calculus questions involving trigonometric functions.

Simplify

Get into the habit of simplifying expressions before doing any further work with them. This should make all subsequent work easier.

Subtraction

Be careful when subtracting one expression from another: ensure that any negative is applied correctly.

Good luck!

Remember that the rewards for passing Higher Mathematics are well worth it! Your pass will help you get the future you want for yourself. In the exam, be confident in your own ability. If you're not sure how to answer a question, trust your instincts and just give it a go anyway – keep calm and don't panic! GOOD LUCK!

HIGHER FOR CfE

2014 Specimen
Question Paper

National
Qualifications
SPECIMEN ONLY

SQ30/H/01

Date — Not applicable

Duration — 1 hour and 10 minutes

**Mathematics
Paper 1
(Non-Calculator)**

Total marks — 60

Attempt ALL questions.

You may NOT use a calculator.

Full credit will be given only to solutions which contain appropriate working.

State the units for your answer where appropriate.

Write your answers clearly in the answer booklet provided. In the answer booklet you must clearly identify the question number you are attempting.

Use **blue** or **black** ink.

Before leaving the examination room you must give your answer booklet to the Invigilator; if you do not you may lose all the marks for this paper.

FORMULAE LIST

Circle:

The equation $x^2 + y^2 + 2gx + 2fy + c = 0$ represents a circle centre $(-g, -f)$ and radius $\sqrt{g^2 + f^2 - c}$.

The equation $(x - a)^2 + (y - b)^2 = r^2$ represents a circle centre (a, b) and radius r.

Scalar Product: $\mathbf{a}.\mathbf{b} = |\mathbf{a}||\mathbf{b}|\cos\theta$, where θ is the angle between $\mathbf{a}$ and $\mathbf{b}$

or $\mathbf{a}.\mathbf{b} = a_1b_1 + a_2b_2 + a_3b_3$ where $\mathbf{a} = \begin{pmatrix} a_1 \\ a_2 \\ a_3 \end{pmatrix}$ and $\mathbf{b} = \begin{pmatrix} b_1 \\ b_2 \\ b_3 \end{pmatrix}$

Trigonometric formulae:

$$\sin(A \pm B) = \sin A \cos B \pm \cos A \sin B$$
$$\cos(A \pm B) = \cos A \cos B \mp \sin A \sin B$$
$$\sin 2A = 2\sin A \cos A$$
$$\cos 2A = \cos^2 A - \sin^2 A$$
$$= 2\cos^2 A - 1$$
$$= 1 - 2\sin^2 A$$

Table of standard derivatives:

$f(x)$	$f'(x)$
$\sin ax$	$a\cos ax$
$\cos ax$	$-a\sin ax$

Table of standard integrals:

$f(x)$	$\int f(x)dx$
$\sin ax$	$-\dfrac{1}{a}\cos ax + C$
$\cos ax$	$\dfrac{1}{a}\sin ax + C$

Ian macdonald.

Attempt ALL questions

MARKS

Total marks — 60

1. Find $\int \dfrac{3x^3+1}{2x^2}\,dx$, $x \neq 0$.   4

2. Find the coordinates of the points of intersection of the curve
   $y = x^3 - 2x^2 + x + 4$ and the line $y = 4x + 4$.   5

   [handwritten:] 0, −1, 3,

   $(0)^3 - 2(0)^2 + (0) + 4 = 4.$

   (4,0)

   $4(3) + 4 = 16$

   3,16.

3. In the diagram, P has coordinates (−6, 3, 9),

   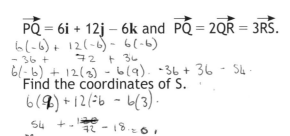

   $\overrightarrow{PQ} = 6\mathbf{i} + 12\mathbf{j} - 6\mathbf{k}$ and $\overrightarrow{PQ} = 2\overrightarrow{QR} = 3\overrightarrow{RS}$.

   [handwritten:]
   $6(-6) + 12(-6) - 6(-6)$
   $-36 + \quad 72 \quad + 36$
   $6(-6) + 12(3) - 6(9). \quad -36 + 36 - 54.$

   Find the coordinates of S.   5

   [handwritten:]
   $6(9) + 12(-6) - 6(3).$
   $54 + -72 - 18 = 0,$

4. Given that $2x^2 + px + p + 6 = 0$ has no real roots, find the range of values for p,
   where $p \in \mathbb{R}$.   4

5. Line l_1 has equation $\sqrt{3}y - x = 0$.

   (a) Line l_2 is perpendicular to l_1. Find the gradient of l_2.   2

   (b) Calculate the angle l_2 makes with the positive direction of the x-axis.   2

6. (a) Find an equivalent expression for $\sin(x + 60)^\circ$.   1

   (b) Hence, or otherwise, determine the exact value of $\sin 105^\circ$.   3

7. (a) Show that $(x + 1)$ is a factor of $x^3 - 13x - 12$.   3

   (b) Factorise $x^3 - 13x - 12$ fully.   2

Page three

MARKS

8. $f(x)$ and $g(x)$ are functions, defined on the set of real numbers, such that

   $f(x) = 1 - \frac{1}{2}x$ and $g(x) = 8x^2 - 3$.

   (a) Given that $h(x) = g(f(x))$, show that $h(x) = 2x^2 - 8x + 5$.   3

   (b) Express $h(x)$ in the form $a(x + p)^2 + q$.   3

   (c) Hence, or otherwise, state the coordinates of the turning point on the graph of $y = h(x)$.   1

   (d) Sketch the graph of $y = h(x) + 3$, showing clearly the coordinates of the turning point and the y-axis intercept.   2

9. (a) AB is a line parallel to the line with equation $y + 3x = 25$.

   A has coordinates $(-1, 10)$.

   Find the equation of AB.   1

   (b) $3y = x + 11$ is the perpendicular bisector of AB.

   Determine the coordinates of B.   5

10. Find the rate of change of the function $f(x) = 4\sin^3 x$ when $x = \dfrac{5\pi}{6}$.   3

11. The diagram shows the graph of $y = f'(x)$. The x-axis is a tangent to this graph.

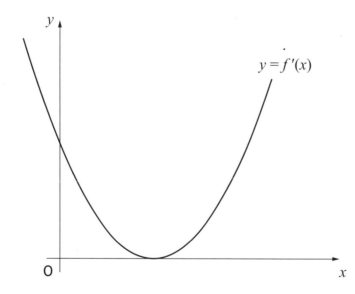

   (a) Explain why the function $f(x)$ is never decreasing.   1

   (b) On a graph of $y = f(x)$, the y-coordinate of the stationary point is negative. Sketch a possible graph for $y = f(x)$.   2

MARKS

12. The voltage, $V(t)$, produced by a generator is described by the function $V(t) = 120 \sin 100 \pi t$, $t > 0$, where t is the time in seconds.

(a) Determine the period of $V(t)$.   2

(b) Find the first three times for which $V(t) = -60$.   6

[END OF SPECIMEN QUESTION PAPER]

National Qualifications
SPECIMEN ONLY

SQ30/H/02

Mathematics
Paper 2

Date — Not applicable

Duration — 1 hour and 30 minutes

Total marks — 70

Attempt ALL questions.

You may use a calculator.

Full credit will be given only to solutions which contain appropriate working.

State the units for your answer where appropriate.

Write your answers clearly in the answer booklet provided. In the answer booklet you must clearly identify the question number you are attempting.

Use **blue** or **black** ink.

Before leaving the examination room you must give your answer booklet to the Invigilator; if you do not you may lose all the marks for this paper.

FORMULAE LIST

Circle:

The equation $x^2 + y^2 + 2gx + 2fy + c = 0$ represents a circle centre $(-g, -f)$ and radius $\sqrt{g^2 + f^2 - c}$.

The equation $(x - a)^2 + (y - b)^2 = r^2$ represents a circle centre (a, b) and radius r.

Scalar Product: $\mathbf{a}.\mathbf{b} = |\mathbf{a}||\mathbf{b}| \cos \theta$, where θ is the angle between $\mathbf{a}$ and $\mathbf{b}$

or $\mathbf{a}.\mathbf{b} = a_1b_1 + a_2b_2 + a_3b_3$ where $\mathbf{a} = \begin{pmatrix} a_1 \\ a_2 \\ a_3 \end{pmatrix}$ and $\mathbf{b} = \begin{pmatrix} b_1 \\ b_2 \\ b_3 \end{pmatrix}$

Trigonometric formulae:

$$\sin (A \pm B) = \sin A \cos B \pm \cos A \sin B$$
$$\cos (A \pm B) = \cos A \cos B \mp \sin A \sin B$$
$$\sin 2A = 2\sin A \cos A$$
$$\cos 2A = \cos^2 A - \sin^2 A$$
$$= 2\cos^2 A - 1$$
$$= 1 - 2\sin^2 A$$

Table of standard derivatives:

$f(x)$	$f'(x)$
$\sin ax$	$a \cos ax$
$\cos ax$	$-a \sin ax$

Table of standard integrals:

$f(x)$	$\int f(x)dx$
$\sin ax$	$-\dfrac{1}{a} \cos ax + C$
$\cos ax$	$\dfrac{1}{a} \sin ax + C$

Attempt ALL questions

MARKS

Total marks — 70

1.

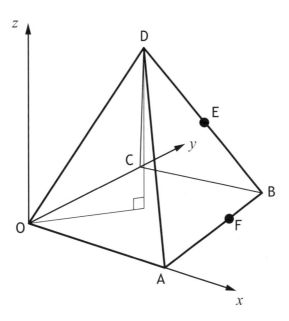

A square based right pyramid is shown in the diagram.

Square OABC has a side length of 60 units with edges OA and OC lying on the x-axis and y-axis respectively.

The coordinates of D are (30, 30, 80).

E is the midpoint of BD and F divides AB in the ratio 2:1.

(a) Find the coordinates of E and F.   **2**

(b) Calculate $\overrightarrow{ED}.\overrightarrow{EF}$.   **2**

(c) Hence, or otherwise, calculate the size of angle DEF.   **4**

2. A wildlife reserve has introduced conservation measures to build up the population of an endangered mammal. Initially the reserve population of the mammal was 2000. By the end of the first year there were 2500 and by the end of the second year there were 2980.

It is believed that the population can be modelled by the recurrence relation:

$$u_{n+1} = au_n + b,$$

where a and b are constants and n is the number of years since the reserve was set up.

(a) Use the information above to find the values of a and b.   **4**

(b) Conservation measures will end if the population stabilises at over 13 000. Will this happen? Justify your answer.   **3**

MARKS

3. The diagram shows the graph of $f(x) = x(x - p)(x - q)^2$.

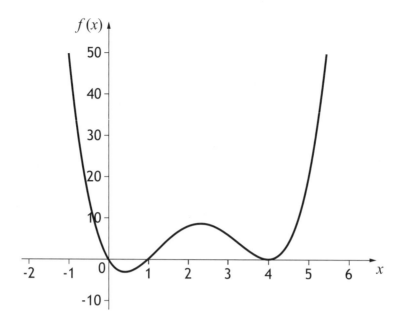

(a) Determine the values of p and q.   1

(b) Find the equation of the tangent to the curve when $x = 1$.   4

4. (a) Express $y = \log_4 2x$ in the form $y = \log_4 x + k$, clearly stating the value of k.   2

(b) Hence, or otherwise, describe the relationship between the graphs of $y = \log_4 2x$ and $y = \log_4 x$.   1

(c) Determine the coordinates of the point where the graph of $y = \log_4 2x$ intersects the x-axis.   2

(d) Sketch and annotate the graph of $y = f^{-1}(x)$, where $f(x) = \log_4 2x$.   3

MARKS

5.

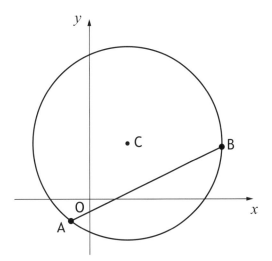

Points A(-1, -1) and B(7, 3) lie on the circumference of a circle with centre C, as shown in the diagram.

(a) Find the equation of the perpendicular bisector of AB.   **4**

CB is parallel to the x-axis.

(b) Find the equation of the circle, passing through A and B, with centre C.   **4**

6. The points A(0, 9, 7), B(5, -1, 2), C(4, 1, 3) and D(x, -2, 2) are such that AB is perpendicular to CD.

Determine the value of x.   **5**

7. Given that $P(t) = 30e^{t-2}$ decide whether each of the statements below is true or false. Justify your answers.

Statement A $P(0) = 30$.

Statement B   When $P(t) = 15$, the only possible value of t is $1\cdot3$ to one decimal place.   **6**

MARKS

8. A design for a new grain container is in the shape of a cylinder with a hemispherical roof and a flat circular base. The radius of the cylinder is r metres, and the height is h metres.

    The volume of the **cylindrical** part of the container needs to be 100 cubic metres.

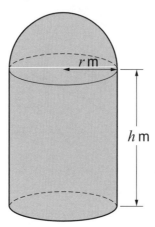

(a) Given that the curved surface area of a hemisphere of radius r is $2\pi r^2$ show that the surface area of metal needed to build the grain container is given by:

$$A = \frac{200}{r} + 3\pi r^2 \text{ square metres}$$

3

(b) Determine the value of r which minimises the amount of metal needed to build the container.

6

9. A sea-life visitor attraction has a new logo in the shape of a shark fin.

   The outline of the logo can be represented by parts of

   - the x axis
   - the curve with equation $y = \cos(2x)$
   - the curve with equation $y = \sin\left(\frac{3}{4}x - \frac{3}{2}\pi\right)$

   as shown in the diagram.

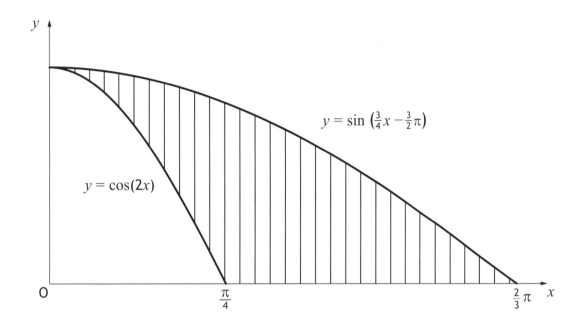

   Calculate the shaded area.   6

MARKS

10. Two sound sources produce the waves $y = \sin t$ and $y = \sqrt{3}\cos t$.

An investigation into the addition of these two waves produces the graph shown, with equation $y = k\cos(t - a)$ for $0 \le t \le 2\pi$.

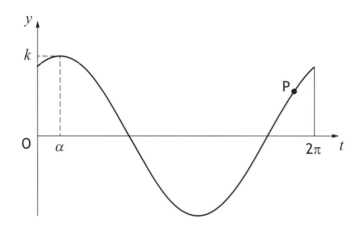

(a) Calculate the values of k and α.   4

The point P has a y-coordinate of 1·2.

(b) Hence calculate the value of the t-coordinate of point P.   4

[END OF SPECIMEN QUESTION PAPER]

Model Paper 1

Whilst this Model Practice Paper has been specially commissioned by Hodder Gibson for use as practice for the Higher (for Curriculum for Excellence) exams, the key reference document remains the SQA Specimen Paper 2014.

National Qualifications
MODEL PAPER 1

Mathematics
Paper 1
(Non-Calculator)

Duration — 1 hour and 10 minutes

Total marks — 60

Attempt ALL questions.

You may NOT use a calculator.

Full credit will be given only to solutions which contain appropriate working.

State the units for your answer where appropriate.

Write your answers clearly in the answer booklet provided. In the answer booklet you must clearly identify the question number you are attempting.

Use **blue** or **black** ink.

Before leaving the examination room you must give your answer booklet to the Invigilator; if you do not you may lose all the marks for this paper.

FORMULAE LIST

Circle:

The equation $x^2 + y^2 + 2gx + 2fy + c = 0$ represents a circle centre $(-g, -f)$ and radius $\sqrt{g^2 + f^2 - c}$.

The equation $(x - a)^2 + (y - b)^2 = r^2$ represents a circle centre (a, b) and radius r.

Scalar Product: $\mathbf{a}.\mathbf{b} = |\mathbf{a}||\mathbf{b}| \cos \theta$, where θ is the angle between $\mathbf{a}$ and $\mathbf{b}$

or $\mathbf{a}.\mathbf{b} = a_1b_1 + a_2b_2 + a_3b_3$ where $\mathbf{a} = \begin{pmatrix} a_1 \\ a_2 \\ a_3 \end{pmatrix}$ and $\mathbf{b} = \begin{pmatrix} b_1 \\ b_2 \\ b_3 \end{pmatrix}$

Trigonometric formulae:

$$\sin (A \pm B) = \sin A \cos B \pm \cos A \sin B$$
$$\cos (A \pm B) = \cos A \cos B \mp \sin A \sin B$$
$$\sin 2A = 2\sin A \cos A$$
$$\cos 2A = \cos^2 A - \sin^2 A$$
$$= 2\cos^2 A - 1$$
$$= 1 - 2\sin^2 A$$

Table of standard derivatives:

$f(x)$	$f'(x)$
$\sin ax$	$a \cos ax$
$\cos ax$	$-a \sin ax$

Table of standard integrals:

$f(x)$	$\int f(x)dx$
$\sin ax$	$-\dfrac{1}{a} \cos ax + C$
$\cos ax$	$\dfrac{1}{a} \sin ax + C$

Attempt ALL questions

Total marks – 60

MARKS

1. ABCD is a parallelogram. A, B and C have coordinates (2,3), (4,7) and (8, 11).

    Find the equation of DC.   3

2. The point Q divides the line joining P(–1, –1, 0) to R(5, 2, –3) in the ratio 2:1.

    Find the coordinates of Q.   3

3. Find the value of k such that the equation $kx^2 + kx + 6$, $k \neq 0$, has equal roots.   4

4. Vectors **u** and **v** are defined by **u** = 3**i** + 2**j** and **v** = 2**i** – 3**j** + 4**k**.

    Determine whether or not **u** and **v** are perpendicular to each other.   2

5. Find $\int \frac{4x^3 - 1}{x^2}\, dx$, $x \neq 0$.   4

6. Functions $f(x) = \dfrac{1}{x - 4}$ and $g(x) = 2x + 3$ are defined on suitable domains.

    (a) Find an expression for $g^{-1}(x)$.   2

    (b) (i)   Find an expression in simplest form for $h(x)$ where $h(x) = f(g)(x))$.   2

    (ii)   Write down any restrictions on the domain of h.   1

7. Explain why the equation $x^2 + y^2 + 2x + 3y + 5 = 0$ does **not** represent a circle.   2

8. A ball is thrown vertically upwards.

    After t seconds its height is h metres, where $h = 1{\cdot}2 + 19{\cdot}6t - 4{\cdot}9t^2$.

    (a) Find the speed of the ball after 1 second.   3

    (b) For how many seconds is the ball travelling upwards?   2

9. (a) Express $7 - 2x - x^2$ in the form $a - (x + b)^2$.   2

    (b) State the maximum value of $7 - 2x - x^2$ and justify your answer.   2

10. The diagram shows part of the graph of $y = \log_b(x + a)$.

Determine the values of a and b.

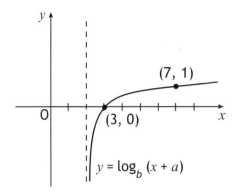

11. The graph of a function f intersects the x-axis at $(-a, 0)$ and $(e, 0)$ as shown.

There is a point of inflexion at $(0, b)$ and a maximum turning point at (c, d).

Sketch the graph of the derived function f'

3

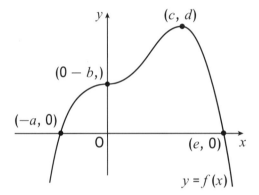

12. A function f is defined on the set of real numbers by $f(x) = x^3 - 3x + 2$.

(a) Find the coordinates of the stationary points on the curve $y = f(x)$ and determine their nature.

6

(b) (i) Show that $(x - 1)$ is a factor of $x^3 - 3x + 2$.

3

(ii) Hence or otherwise factorise $x^3 - 3x + 2$ fully.

2

(c) State the coordinates of the points where the curve with equation $y = f(x)$ meets both the axes and hence sketch the curve.

4

13. In the diagram   **MARKS**

- angle DEC = angle CEB = $x°$
- angle CDE = angle BEA = 90°
- CD = 1 unit
- DE = 3 units.

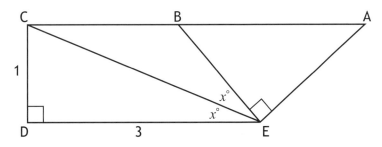

By writing angle DEA in terms of $x°$, find the exact value of cos(DEA).   **7**

[END OF MODEL QUESTION PAPER]

National
Qualifications
MODEL PAPER 1

**Mathematics
Paper 2**

Duration — 1 hour and 30 minutes

Total marks — 70

Attempt ALL questions.

You may use a calculator.

Full credit will be given only to solutions which contain appropriate working.

State the units for your answer where appropriate.

Write your answers clearly in the answer booklet provided. In the answer booklet you must clearly identify the question number you are attempting.

Use **blue** or **black** ink.

Before leaving the examination room you must give your answer booklet to the Invigilator; if you do not you may lose all the marks for this paper.

FORMULAE LIST

Circle:

The equation $x^2 + y^2 + 2gx + 2fy + c = 0$ represents a circle centre $(-g, -f)$ and radius $\sqrt{g^2 + f^2 - c}$.

The equation $(x - a)^2 + (y - b)^2 = r^2$ represents a circle centre (a, b) and radius r.

Scalar Product: $\mathbf{a}.\mathbf{b} = |\mathbf{a}||\mathbf{b}| \cos \theta$, where θ is the angle between $\mathbf{a}$ and $\mathbf{b}$

or $\mathbf{a}.\mathbf{b} = a_1b_1 + a_2b_2 + a_3b_3$ where $\mathbf{a} = \begin{pmatrix} a_1 \\ a_2 \\ a_3 \end{pmatrix}$ and $\mathbf{b} = \begin{pmatrix} b_1 \\ b_2 \\ b_3 \end{pmatrix}$

Trigonometric formulae:

$$\sin (A \pm B) = \sin A \cos B \pm \cos A \sin B$$
$$\cos (A \pm B) = \cos A \cos B \mp \sin A \sin B$$
$$\sin 2A = 2\sin A \cos A$$
$$\cos 2A = \cos^2 A - \sin^2 A$$
$$= 2\cos^2 A - 1$$
$$= 1 - 2\sin^2 A$$

Table of standard derivatives:

$f(x)$	$f'(x)$
$\sin ax$	$a \cos ax$
$\cos ax$	$-a \sin ax$

Table of standard integrals:

$f(x)$	$\int f(x)dx$
$\sin ax$	$-\dfrac{1}{a} \cos ax + C$
$\cos ax$	$\dfrac{1}{a} \sin ax + C$

Attempt ALL questions

MARKS

Total marks – 70

1. The vertices of triangle ABC are A(7, 9), B(–3, –1) and C(5, –5) as shown in the diagram.

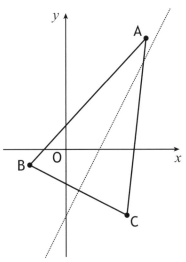

The broken line represents the perpendicular bisector of BC.

(a) Show that the equation of the perpendicular bisector of BC is $y = 2x - 5$.   4

(b) Find the equation of the median from C.   3

(c) Find the coordinates of the point of intersection of the perpendicular bisector of BC and the median from C.   3

2. D,OABC is a square based pyramid as shown in the diagram.

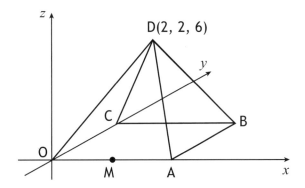

O is the origin, D is the point (2, 2, 6) and OA = 4 units.

M is the midpoint of OA.

(a) State the coordinates of B.   1

(b) Express $\overrightarrow{DB}$ and $\overrightarrow{DM}$ in component form.   3

(c) Find the size of angle BDM.   5

3. A man decides to plant a number of fast-growing trees as a boundary between his property and the property of his next door neighbour. He has been warned, however, by the local garden centre that, during any year, the trees are expected to increase in height by 0·5 metres. In response to this warning, he decides to trim 20% off the height of the trees at the start of any year.

MARKS

(a) If he adopts the "20% pruning policy", to what height will he expect the trees to grow in the long run?

3

(b) His neighbour is concerned that the trees are growing at an alarming rate and wants assurances that the trees will grow no taller than 2 metres.

What is the minimum percentage that the trees will need to be trimmed each year so as to meet this condition?

3

4. The diagram shows the curve with equation $y = x^3 - x^2 - 4x + 4$ and the line with equation $y = 2x + 4$.

The curve and the line intersect at the points $(-2, 0)$, $(0, 4)$ and $(3, 10)$.

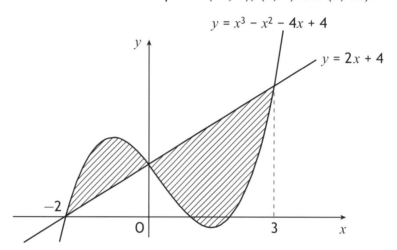

Calculate the total shaded area.

10

5. (a) $12 \cos x° - 5 \sin x°$ can be expressed in the form $k \cos (x + a)°$, where $k > 0$ and $0 \le a < 360$.

Calculate the values of k and a.

4

(b) (i) Hence state the maximum and minimum values of $12 \cos x° - 5 \sin x°$.

1

(ii) Determine the values of x, in the interval $0 \le x < 360$ at which these maximum and minimum values occur.

2

6. Find the value of $\int_0^2 \sin(4x + 1)dx$.

4

7. (a) (i) Show that the line with the equation $y = 3 - x$ is a tangent to the circle with the equation $x^2 + y^2 + 14x + 4y - 19 = 0$

MARKS
4

   (ii) Find the coordinates of the point of contact, P.

1

   (b) Relative to a suitable set of coordinate axes, the diagram below shows the circle from (a) and a second smaller circle with centre C.

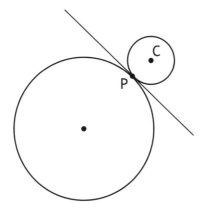

   The line $y = 3 - x$ is a common tangent at the point P.

   The radius of the larger circle is three times the radius of the smaller circle.

   Find the equation of the smaller circle.

6

8. The amount A_t micrograms of a certain radioactive substance remaining after t years decreases according to the formula $A_t = A_0 e^{-0.002t}$, where A_0 is the amount present initially.

   (a) If 600 micrograms are left after 1000 years, how many micrograms were present initially?

3

   (b) The half-life of a substance is the time taken for the amount to decrease to half of its initial amount. What is the half-life of this substance?

5

9. Solve $2 \cos 2x - 5 \cos x - 4 = 0$ for $0 \le x < 2\pi$

5

[END OF MODEL QUESTION PAPER]

HIGHER FOR CfE

Model Paper 2

Whilst this Model Practice Paper has been specially commissioned by Hodder Gibson for use as practice for the Higher (for Curriculum for Excellence) exams, the key reference document remains the SQA Specimen Paper 2014.

National
Qualifications
MODEL PAPER 2

Mathematics
Paper 1
(Non-Calculator)

Duration — 1 hour and 10 minutes

Total marks — 60

Attempt ALL questions.

You may NOT use a calculator.

Full credit will be given only to solutions which contain appropriate working.

State the units for your answer where appropriate.

Write your answers clearly in the answer booklet provided. In the answer booklet you must clearly identify the question number you are attempting.

Use **blue** or **black** ink.

Before leaving the examination room you must give your answer booklet to the Invigilator; if you do not you may lose all the marks for this paper.

FORMULAE LIST

Circle:

The equation $x^2 + y^2 + 2gx + 2fy + c = 0$ represents a circle centre $(-g, -f)$ and radius $\sqrt{g^2 + f^2 - c}$.

The equation $(x - a)^2 + (y - b)^2 = r^2$ represents a circle centre (a, b) and radius r.

Scalar Product: $\mathbf{a}.\mathbf{b} = |\mathbf{a}||\mathbf{b}| \cos \theta$, where θ is the angle between $\mathbf{a}$ and $\mathbf{b}$

or $\mathbf{a}.\mathbf{b} = a_1b_1 + a_2b_2 + a_3b_3$ where $\mathbf{a} = \begin{pmatrix} a_1 \\ a_2 \\ a_3 \end{pmatrix}$ and $\mathbf{b} = \begin{pmatrix} b_1 \\ b_2 \\ b_3 \end{pmatrix}$

Trigonometric formulae:

$$\sin (A \pm B) = \sin A \cos B \pm \cos A \sin B$$
$$\cos (A \pm B) = \cos A \cos B \mp \sin A \sin B$$
$$\sin 2A = 2\sin A \cos A$$
$$\cos 2A = \cos^2 A - \sin^2 A$$
$$= 2\cos^2 A - 1$$
$$= 1 - 2\sin^2 A$$

Table of standard derivatives:

$f(x)$	$f'(x)$
$\sin ax$	$a \cos ax$
$\cos ax$	$-a \sin ax$

Table of standard integrals:

$f(x)$	$\int f(x)dx$
$\sin ax$	$-\dfrac{1}{a} \cos ax + C$
$\cos ax$	$\dfrac{1}{a} \sin ax + C$

Attempt ALL questions

MARKS

Total marks – 60

1. Triangle ABC has vertices A(–1,12), B(–2, –5) and C(7, –2).

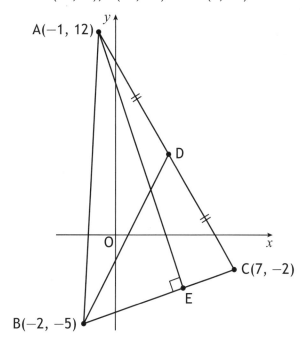

(a) Find the equation of the median BD. 3

(b) Find the equation of the altitude AE. 3

(c) Find the coordinates of the point of intersection of BD and AE. 3

2. Relative to a suitable coordinate system, A and B are the points (–2, 1, –1) and (1, 3, 2) respectively.

A, B and C are collinear points and C is positioned such that BC = 2AB.

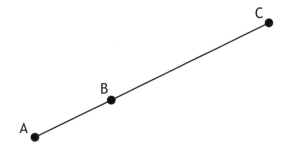

Find the coordinates of C. 4

Page three

3. The diagram shows two right-angled triangles with angles c and d marked as shown.   **MARKS**

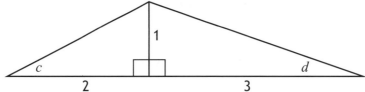

(a) Find the exact value of $\sin(c + d)$.   4

(b) (i) Find the exact value of $\sin 2c$.   2

   (ii) Show that $\cos 2d$ has the same exact value.   2

4. The diagram shows a sketch of part of the graph of a trigonometric function whose equation is of the form $y = a \sin bx + c$.

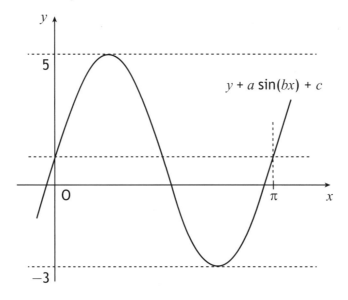

$y + a \sin(bx) + c$

Determine the values of a, b and c.   3

MARKS

5. The graph shown has equation $y = x^3 - 6x + 4x + 1$.

The total shaded area is bounded by the curve, the x-axis, the y-axis and the line $x = 2$.

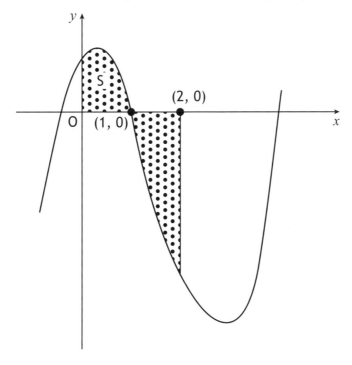

(a) Calculate the shaded area labelled S.   4

(b) Hence find the total shaded area.   3

6. Show that the line with the equation $y = 2x + 1$ does not intersect with the parabola with equation $y = x^2 + 3x + 4$.   5

7. Find $\int_0^1 \dfrac{dx}{(3x + 1)^{\frac{1}{2}}}$.   4

8. Find algebraically the values of x for which the function $f(x) = 2x^3 - 3x^2 - 36x$ is increasing.   4

9. Evaluate $\log_5 2 + \log_5 50 - \log_5 4$.   3

10. Solve $2 \sin 3x - 1 = 0$ for $0 \leq x \leq \pi$.   4

11. The circles with the equations $(x - 3)^2 + (y - 4)^2 = 25$ and $x^2 + y^2 - kx - 8y - 2k = 0$ have the same centre.

Determine the radius of the larger circle.   4

MARKS

12. The diagram shows a sketch of function $y = f(x)$.

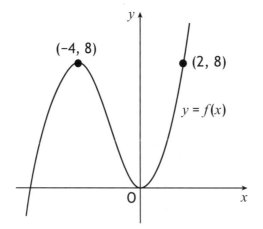

(a) Copy the diagram and on to it sketch the graph of $y = f(2x)$.   **2**

(b) Copy the diagram again and, this time, sketch the graph of $y = 1 - f(2x)$.   **3**

[END OF MODEL QUESTION PAPER]

National
Qualifications
MODEL PAPER 2

Mathematics
Paper 2

Duration — 1 hour and 30 minutes

Total marks — 70

Attempt ALL questions.

You may use a calculator.

Full credit will be given only to solutions which contain appropriate working.

State the units for your answer where appropriate.

Write your answers clearly in the answer booklet provided. In the answer booklet you must clearly identify the question number you are attempting.

Use **blue** or **black** ink.

Before leaving the examination room you must give your answer booklet to the Invigilator; if you do not you may lose all the marks for this paper.

FORMULAE LIST

Circle:

The equation $x^2 + y^2 + 2gx + 2fy + c = 0$ represents a circle centre $(-g, -f)$ and radius $\sqrt{g^2 + f^2 - c}$.

The equation $(x - a)^2 + (y - b)^2 = r^2$ represents a circle centre (a, b) and radius r.

Scalar Product: $\mathbf{a.b} = |\mathbf{a}||\mathbf{b}| \cos \theta$, where θ is the angle between $\mathbf{a}$ and $\mathbf{b}$

or $\mathbf{a.b} = a_1b_1 + a_2b_2 + a_3b_3$ where $\mathbf{a} = \begin{pmatrix} a_1 \\ a_2 \\ a_3 \end{pmatrix}$ and $\mathbf{b} = \begin{pmatrix} b_1 \\ b_2 \\ b_3 \end{pmatrix}$

Trigonometric formulae:
$$\sin (A \pm B) = \sin A \cos B \pm \cos A \sin B$$
$$\cos (A \pm B) = \cos A \cos B \mp \sin A \sin B$$
$$\sin 2A = 2\sin A \cos A$$
$$\cos 2A = \cos^2 A - \sin^2 A$$
$$= 2\cos^2 A - 1$$
$$= 1 - 2\sin^2 A$$

Table of standard derivatives:

$f(x)$	$f'(x)$
$\sin ax$	$a \cos ax$
$\cos ax$	$-a \sin ax$

Table of standard integrals:

$f(x)$	$\int f(x)dx$
$\sin ax$	$-\dfrac{1}{a} \cos ax + C$
$\cos ax$	$\dfrac{1}{a} \sin ax + C$

Attempt ALL questions   MARKS

Total marks – 70

1. The diagram shows a cuboid OPQR,STUV relative to the coordinate axes.

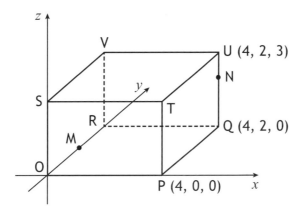

P is the point (4, 0, 0), Q is (4, 2, 0) and U is (4, 2, 3).

M is the midpoint of OR.

N is the point on UQ such that UN = $\frac{1}{3}$UQ.

(a) State the coordinates of M and N.   2

(b) Express $\overrightarrow{VM}$ and $\overrightarrow{VN}$ in component form.   2

(c) Calculate the size of angle MVN.   5

2. (a) Given that $x + 2$ is a factor of $2x^3 + x^2 + kx + 2$, find the value of k.   3

(b) Hence solve the equation $2x^3 + x^2 + kx + 2 = 0$ when k takes this value.   2

3. Given that $y = 3 \sin x + \cos 2x$, find $\frac{dy}{dx}$.   3

4. On a suitable set of real numbers, functions f, g and h are defined by

$$f(x) = \frac{1}{x+2}, \ g(x) = \frac{1}{x} - 2 \ \text{and} \ h(x) = \frac{x^2 - 1}{2}.$$

Find an expression for

(a) $f(g(x))$ in its simplest form   3

(b) $h^{-1}(x)$.   3

5. The curve $y = f(x)$ is such that $\frac{dy}{dx} = 4x - 6x^2$. The curve passes through the point (−1, 9).

Express y in terms of x.   4

MARKS

6. On the first day of March, a bank loans a man £2500 at a fixed rate of interest of 1·5% per month. This interest is added on the last day of each month and is calculated on the amount due on the first day of the month. He agrees to make repayments on the first day of each subsequent month. Each repayment is £300, except for the smaller final amount which will pay off the loan.

   (a) The amount that he owes at the start of each month is taken to be the amount still owed just after the monthly repayment has been made.

   Let u_n and u_{n+1} represent the amounts that he owes at the starts of two successive months. Write down a recurrence relation involving u_{n+1} and u_n.   **2**

   (b) Find the date and amount of the final payment.   **4**

7. (a) A chord joins the points A(1, 0) and B(5, 4) on the circle as shown in the diagram.

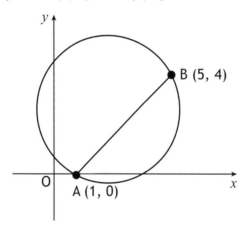

   Show that the equation of the perpendicular bisector of chord AB is $x + y = 5$.   **4**

   (b) The point C is the centre of this circle.

   The tangent at the point A on the circle has the equation $x + 3y = 1$.

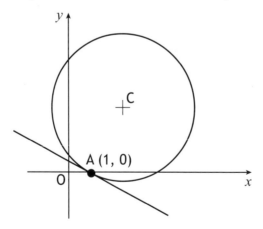

   Find the equation of the radius CA.   **4**

   (c) (i) Determine the coordinates of the point C.   **2**

   (ii) Find the equation of the circle.   **2**

8. (a) Express $3 \cos x° + 5 \sin x°$ in the form $k \cos(x - a)°$ where $k > 0$ and $0 \leq a \leq 90$.

MARKS

4

(b) Hence solve the equation $3 \cos x° + 5 \sin x° = 4$ for $0 \leq x \leq 90$.

3

9. Variables x and y are related by the equation $y = kx^n$.

The graph of $\log_2 y$ against $\log_2 x$ is a straight line through the points $(0, 5)$ and $(4, 7)$, as shown in the diagram.

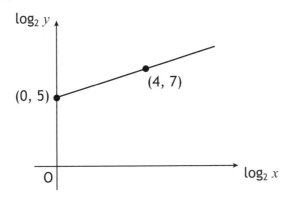

Find the values of k and n.

5

10. The value V (in £ million) of a cruise ship t years after launch is given by the formula $V = 252e^{-0.06335t}$.

(a) What was its value when launched?

1

(b) The owners decide to sell the ship once its value falls below £20 million.

After how many years will it be sold?

4

11. An open cuboid measures internally x units by $2x$ units by h units and has an inner surface area of 12 units^2.

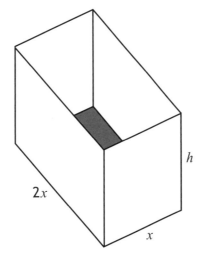

(a) Show that the volume, V units^3, of the cuboid is given by $V(x) = \frac{2}{3}x(6 - x^2)$.

3

(b) Find the exact value of x for which this volume is a maximum.

5

[END OF MODEL QUESTION PAPER]

National Qualifications
MODEL PAPER 3

Mathematics
Paper 1
(Non-Calculator)

Duration — 1 hour and 10 minutes

Total marks — 60

Attempt ALL questions.

You may NOT use a calculator.

Full credit will be given only to solutions which contain appropriate working.

State the units for your answer where appropriate.

Write your answers clearly in the answer booklet provided. In the answer booklet you must clearly identify the question number you are attempting.

Use **blue** or **black** ink.

Before leaving the examination room you must give your answer booklet to the Invigilator; if you do not you may lose all the marks for this paper.

FORMULAE LIST

Circle:

The equation $x^2 + y^2 + 2gx + 2fy + c = 0$ represents a circle centre $(-g, -f)$ and radius $\sqrt{g^2 + f^2 - c}$.

The equation $(x - a)^2 + (y - b)^2 = r^2$ represents a circle centre (a, b) and radius r.

Scalar Product: $\mathbf{a}.\mathbf{b} = |\mathbf{a}||\mathbf{b}| \cos \theta$, where θ is the angle between $\mathbf{a}$ and $\mathbf{b}$

or $\mathbf{a}.\mathbf{b} = a_1b_1 + a_2b_2 + a_3b_3$ where $\mathbf{a} = \begin{pmatrix} a_1 \\ a_2 \\ a_3 \end{pmatrix}$ and $\mathbf{b} = \begin{pmatrix} b_1 \\ b_2 \\ b_3 \end{pmatrix}$

Trigonometric formulae:

$$\sin (A \pm B) = \sin A \cos B \pm \cos A \sin B$$
$$\cos (A \pm B) = \cos A \cos B \mp \sin A \sin B$$
$$\sin 2A = 2\sin A \cos A$$
$$\cos 2A = \cos^2 A - \sin^2 A$$
$$= 2\cos^2 A - 1$$
$$= 1 - 2\sin^2 A$$

Table of standard derivatives:

$f(x)$	$f'(x)$
$\sin ax$	$a \cos ax$
$\cos ax$	$-a \sin ax$

Table of standard integrals:

$f(x)$	$\int f(x)dx$
$\sin ax$	$-\dfrac{1}{a} \cos ax + C$
$\cos ax$	$\dfrac{1}{a} \sin ax + C$

Attempt ALL questions

Total marks — 60

MARKS

1. Find the equation of the line ST, where T is the point $(-2, 0)$ and angle STO is $60°$.　　3

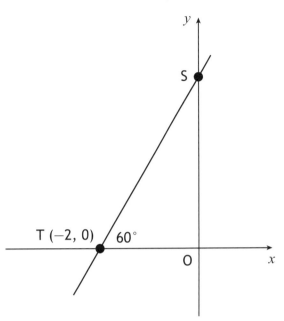

2. VABCD is a pyramid with rectangular base ABCD.

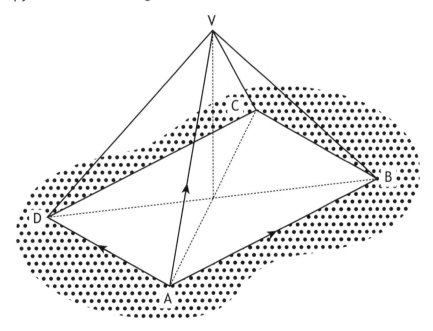

The vectors $\overrightarrow{AB}$, $\overrightarrow{AD}$ and $\overrightarrow{AV}$ are given by

$\overrightarrow{AB} = 8\mathbf{i} + 2\mathbf{j} + 2\mathbf{k}$, $\overrightarrow{AD} = -2\mathbf{i} + 10\mathbf{j} - 2\mathbf{k}$ and $\overrightarrow{AV} = \mathbf{i} + 7\mathbf{j} + 7\mathbf{k}$.

Express $\overrightarrow{CV}$ in component form.

3

3. Given that $f(x) = 3\sqrt{x}$, find $f'(4)$.

3

4. Express $2x^2 + 4x - 3$ in the form $a(x + b)^2 + c$.

3

5. Functions f and g, defined on suitable domains, are given by $f(x) = x^2 + 1$ and $g(x) = 1 - 2x$.

Find in its simplest form:

(a) $g(f(x))$;

2

(b) $g(g(x))$.

2

6. The diagram shows the graph of a function f.

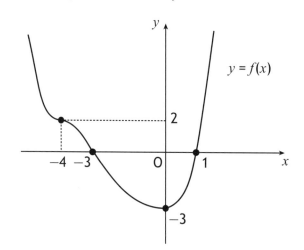

f has a minimum turning point at $(0, -3)$ and a point of inflexion at $(-4, 2)$.

(a) Sketch the graph of $y = f(-x)$.

2

(b) On the same diagram, sketch the graph of $y = 2f(-x)$.

2

7. If $x°$ is an acute angle such that $\tan x° = \dfrac{4}{3}$, show that the exact value of $\cos(x + 30)°$ is $\dfrac{3\sqrt{3} - 4}{10}$.

3

MARKS

8. (a) A sequence is defined by $u_{n+1} = -\frac{1}{2}u_n$ with $u_0 = -16$.

Write down the values of u_1 and u_2. **1**

(b) A second sequence is given by 4, 5, 7, 11, ...

It is generated by the recurrence relation $v_{n+1} = pv_n + q$ with $v_1 = 4$.

Find the values of p and q. **3**

(c) Either the sequence in (a) or the sequence in (b) has a limit.

(i) Calculate this limit. **2**

(ii) Why does the other sequence not have a limit? **1**

9. (a) (i) Show that $x = 1$ is a root of $x^3 + 8x^2 + 11x - 20 = 0$. **1**

(ii) Hence factorise $x^3 + 8x^2 + 11x - 20$ fully. **3**

(b) Solve $\log_2(x + 3) + \log_2(x^2 + 5x - 4) = 3$. **5**

10. The graph of $y = f(x)$ passes through the point $\left(\frac{\pi}{9}, 1\right)$.

Given that $f'(x) = \sin 3x$, express y in terms of x. **4**

11. (a) Express $\sin x - \sqrt{3}\cos x$ in the form $k\sin(x - a)$ where $k > 0$ and $0 \le a \le 2\pi$. **4**

(b) Hence, or otherwise, sketch the curve with the equation $y = 3 + \sin x - \sqrt{3}\cos x$ in the interval $0 \le x \le 2\pi$. **5**

12. Vectors **a** and **c** are represented by two sides of an equilateral triangle with sides of length 3 units, as shown in the diagram.

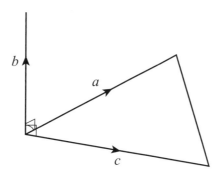

Vector **b** is 2 units long and **b** is perpendicular to both **a** and **c**.

Evaluate the scalar product **a**.(**a** + **b** + **c**). **4**

13. The diagram shows the graph of the function $f(x) = \dfrac{1}{x+1}$, $x \neq -1$.

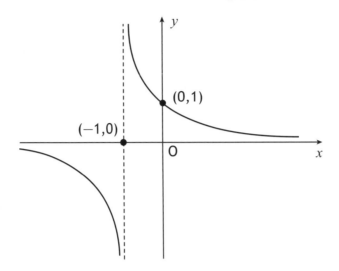

Prove that the function f is decreasing for all values of x except $x = -1$.   **4**

[END OF MODEL QUESTION PAPER]

National Qualifications MODEL PAPER 3

Mathematics Paper 2

Duration — 1 hour and 30 minutes

Total marks — 70

Attempt ALL questions.

You may use a calculator.

Full credit will be given only to solutions which contain appropriate working.

State the units for your answer where appropriate.

Write your answers clearly in the answer booklet provided. In the answer booklet you must clearly identify the question number you are attempting.

Use **blue** or **black** ink.

Before leaving the examination room you must give your answer booklet to the Invigilator; if you do not you may lose all the marks for this paper.

FORMULAE LIST

Circle:

The equation $x^2 + y^2 + 2gx + 2fy + c = 0$ represents a circle centre $(-g, -f)$ and radius $\sqrt{g^2 + f^2 - c}$.

The equation $(x - a)^2 + (y - b)^2 = r^2$ represents a circle centre (a, b) and radius r.

Scalar Product: $\mathbf{a}.\mathbf{b} = |\mathbf{a}||\mathbf{b}| \cos \theta$, where θ is the angle between $\mathbf{a}$ and $\mathbf{b}$

or $\mathbf{a}.\mathbf{b} = a_1b_1 + a_2b_2 + a_3b_3$ where $\mathbf{a} = \begin{pmatrix} a_1 \\ a_2 \\ a_3 \end{pmatrix}$ and $\mathbf{b} = \begin{pmatrix} b_1 \\ b_2 \\ b_3 \end{pmatrix}$

Trigonometric formulae:

$$\sin (A \pm B) = \sin A \cos B \pm \cos A \sin B$$
$$\cos (A \pm B) = \cos A \cos B \mp \sin A \sin B$$
$$\sin 2A = 2\sin A \cos A$$
$$\cos 2A = \cos^2 A - \sin^2 A$$
$$= 2\cos^2 A - 1$$
$$= 1 - 2\sin^2 A$$

Table of standard derivatives:

$f(x)$	$f'(x)$
$\sin ax$	$a \cos ax$
$\cos ax$	$-a \sin ax$

Table of standard integrals:

$f(x)$	$\int f(x)dx$
$\sin ax$	$-\dfrac{1}{a} \cos ax + C$
$\cos ax$	$\dfrac{1}{a} \sin ax + C$

Attempt ALL questions

MARKS

Total marks — 70

1. (a) (i) Show that the points A(−7, −8, 1), T(3, 2, 5) and B(18, 17, 11) are collinear.   **3**

   (ii) Find the ratio in which T divides AB.   **1**

   (b) The point C lies on the x-axis.

   If TB and TC are perpendicular, find the coordinates of C.   **5**

2. The point $P(x, y)$ lies on the curve with the equation y = $6x^2 - x^3$.

   (a) Find the value of x for which the gradient of the tangent at P is 12.   **5**

   (b) Hence find the equation of the tangent at P.   **2**

3. Prove that the roots of the equation $2x^2 + px - 3 = 0$ are real for all values of p.   **4**

4. (a) Find the equation of l_1, the perpendicular bisector of the line joining P(3, −3) to Q(−1, 9).   **4**

   (b) Find the equation of l_2 which is parallel to PQ and passes through R(1, −2).   **2**

   (c) Find the point of intersection of l_1 and l_2.   **3**

   (d) Hence find the shortest distance between PQ and l_2.   **2**

5. (a) Write down the centre and calculate the radius of the circle with the equation $x^2 + y^2 + 8x + 4y - 38 = 0$.   **2**

   (b) A second circle has the equation $(x - 4)^2 + (y - 6)^2 = 26$.

   Find the distance between the centres of these two circles and hence show that the circles intersect.   **4**

   (c) The line with the equation $y = 4 - x$ is a common chord passing through the points of intersection of the two circles.

   Find the coordinates of the points of intersection of the two circles.   **5**

6. Solve algebraically the equation $\sin 2x = 2\cos^2 x$ for $0 \le x < 2\pi$.   **6**

7. It is claimed that a wheel is made from wood which is over 1000 years old.   **MARKS**

    To test this claim, carbon dating is used.

    The formula $A(t) = A_0e^{-0.000124t}$ is used to determine the age of the wood, where A_0 is the amount of carbon in any living tree, $A(t)$ is the amount of carbon in the wood being dated and t is the age of the wood in years.

    For the wheel, it was found that $A(t)$ was 88% of the amount of carbon in a living tree.

    Is the claim true?   **5**

8. In the diagram, Q lies on the line joining (0, 6) and (3, 0).

    OPQR is a rectangle, where P and R lie on the axes and OR = t.

    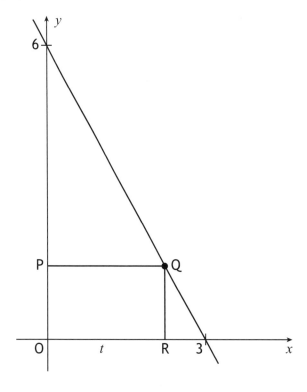

    (a) Show that QR = 6 − 2t.   **3**

    (b) Find the coordinates of Q for which the rectangle has a maximum area.   **6**

MARKS

9. An architectural feature of a building is a wall with arched windows.

   The curved edge of each window is parabolic.

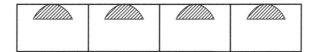

   The second diagram shows one such window.

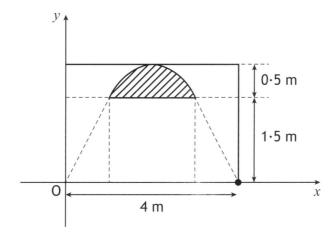

   The shaded part represents the glass.

   The top edge of the window is part of the parabola with the equation $y = 2x - \dfrac{1}{2}x^2$.

   Find the area in square metres of the glass in one window.   **8**

[END OF MODEL QUESTION PAPER]

HIGHER FOR CfE | ANSWER SECTION

SQA AND HODDER GIBSON HIGHER FOR CfE MATHEMATICS 2014

HIGHER FOR CfE MATHEMATICS
SPECIMEN QUESTION PAPER

Paper 1 (Non-Calculator)

Question			Marking scheme. Give one mark for each •	Max mark	Illustration of evidence for awarding a mark at each •
1.			Ans: $\frac{3}{4}x^2 - \frac{1}{2}x^{-1} + C$	4	$\int \frac{Bx^3 + 1}{2x^2}\,dx$
			•^{1} preparation for integration		•^{1} $\frac{3}{2}x + \frac{1}{2}x^{-2}$
			•^{2} correct integration of first term		•^{2} $\frac{3}{2} \times \frac{x^2}{2} + \ldots$
			•^{3} correct integration of second term		•^{3} $\ldots + \frac{1}{2} \times \frac{x^{-1}}{-1}$
			•^{4} includes constant of integration		•^{4} $\frac{3}{4}x^2 - \frac{1}{2}x^{-1} + C$
2.			Ans: $(-1,0),(0,4),(3,16)$	5	
			•^{1} sets equation of curve equal to equation of line		•^{1} $x^3 - 2x^2 + x + 4 = 4x + 4$
			•^{2} equates to zero		•^{2} $x^3 - 2x^2 - 3x = 0$
			•^{3} factorises fully		•^{3} $x(x+1)(x-3) = 0$
			•^{4} calculates x-coordinates		•^{4} $x = 0, x = -1, x = 3$
			•^{5} calculates y-coordinates		•^{5} $(0,4),(-1,0),(3,16)$
3.			Ans: S(5, 25, −2)	5	
			•^{1} find coordinate of Q or component vector $\mathbf{q}$		•^{1} $\mathbf{q} = \mathbf{p} + \overrightarrow{PQ} = \begin{pmatrix} 0 \\ 15 \\ 3 \end{pmatrix}$ or Q$(0,15,3)$
			•^{2} sets up vector equation for $\mathbf{r}$		•^{2} $\mathbf{r} = \mathbf{q} + \overrightarrow{QR} = \begin{pmatrix} 0 \\ 15 \\ 3 \end{pmatrix} + \begin{pmatrix} 3 \\ 6 \\ -3 \end{pmatrix}$
			•^{3} find coordinate of R or component vector $\mathbf{r}$		•^{3} $\mathbf{r} = \begin{pmatrix} 3 \\ 21 \\ 0 \end{pmatrix}$ or R$(3,21,0)$
			•^{4} sets up vector equation for $\mathbf{s}$		•^{4} $\mathbf{s} = \mathbf{r} + \overrightarrow{RS} = \begin{pmatrix} 3 \\ 21 \\ 0 \end{pmatrix} + \begin{pmatrix} 2 \\ 4 \\ -2 \end{pmatrix}$
			•^{5} find coordinate of S		•^{5} S $(5,25,-2)$

Question			Marking scheme. Give one mark for each •	Max mark	Illustration of evidence for awarding a mark at each •
4.			Ans: $-4 < p < 12$ •¹ know discriminant < 0 •² simplify •³ factorise LHS •⁴ correct range	4	•¹ $b^2 - 4ac < 0$ and $a = 2$, $b = p$, $c = p+6$ stated or implied by •² •² $p^2 - 8p - 48 < 0$ •³ $(p-12)(p+4) < 0$ •⁴ $-4 < p < 12$
5.	(a)		Ans: $m_{l_2} = -\sqrt{3}$ •¹ rearranging equation to calculate gradient of line l_1 •² calculating gradient of l_2	2	•¹ $y = \frac{1}{\sqrt{3}}x \quad m = \frac{1}{\sqrt{3}}$ •² $m_{l_2} = -\sqrt{3}$
	(b)		Ans: $\theta = \frac{2\pi}{3}$ or $120°$ •³ using $m = \tan\theta$ •⁴ calculating angle	2	•³ $\tan\theta = -\sqrt{3}$ •⁴ $\theta = \frac{2\pi}{3}$ or $120°$
6.	(a) (b)		Ans: $\frac{1+\sqrt{3}}{2\sqrt{2}}$ or $\frac{\sqrt{2}+\sqrt{6}}{4}$ •¹ correct expansion •² any expression equivalent to $\sin 105°$ •³ correct exact value equivalents •⁴ correct answer	4	•¹ $\sin x° \cos 60° + \cos x° \sin 60°$ •² $\sin(45+60)°$ or equivalent •³ $\frac{1}{\sqrt{2}} \times \frac{1}{2} + \frac{1}{\sqrt{2}} \times \frac{\sqrt{3}}{2}$ •⁴ $\frac{1+\sqrt{3}}{2\sqrt{2}}$ or $\frac{\sqrt{2}+\sqrt{6}}{4}$
7.	(a)		•¹ know to use $x = -1$ •² complete synthetic division •³ recognition of zero remainder	3	•¹ $\begin{array}{r|rrrr} -1 & 1 & 0 & -13 & -12 \\ & & -1 & 1 & 12 \\ \hline & 1 & -1 & -12 & 0 \end{array}$ •² $\begin{array}{r|rrrr} -1 & 1 & 0 & -13 & -12 \\ & & -1 & 1 & 12 \\ \hline & 1 & -1 & -12 & 0 \end{array}$ •³ $(x+1)$ is a factor as remainder is zero
	(b)		Ans: $(x+1)(x+3)(x-4)$ •⁴ identify quotient •⁵ factorised fully	2	•⁴ $x^2 - x - 12$ •⁵ $(x+1)(x+3)(x-4)$
	Notes		Alternative methods of showing $(x+1)$ is a factor, such as long division, inspection and evaluating are perfectly acceptable.		

Question			Marking scheme. Give one mark for each •	Max mark	Illustration of evidence for awarding a mark at each •
8.	(a)		Ans: $h(x) = 2x^2 - 8x + 5$ •[1] correct substitution •[2] squaring •[3] expanding and simplifying	3	•[1] $h(x) = 8\left(1 - \frac{1}{2}x\right)^2 - 3$ •[2] $1 - x + \frac{1}{4}x^2$ •[3] $h(x) = 2x^2 - 8x + 5$
	(b)		Ans: $2(x-2)^2 - 3$ •[4] identify common factor •[5] complete the square •[6] process for q	3	•[4] $2(x^2 - 4x...$ stated or implied by •[3] •[5] $2(x^2 - 2)^2...$ •[6] $2(x^2 - 2)^2 - 3$
	Notes		Values for p and q must be consistent with the value for a.		
	(c)		Ans: $(2, -3)$ •[7] state turning point	1	•[7] $(2, -3)$
	(d)		Ans: •[8] correct shape •[9] annotation, including y-axis intercept	2	 •[8] parabola with minimum turning point labelled (positioned consistently with answer to (b)) •[9] $(0,8)$
9.	(a)		Ans: $y - 10 = -3(x+1)$ •[1] finding equation of line	1	•[1] $y - 10 = -3(x+1)$ or equivalent
	(b)		Ans: $B(3,-2)$ •[2] use of simultaneous equations •[3] solving to find one coordinate of midpoint •[4] finding remaining coordinate of midpoint •[5] using midpoint formula or 'stepping out' •[6] finding coordinates of B	5	•[2] $y = -3x + 7$ and $3y = x + 11$ •[3] either $x = 1$ or $y = 4$ •[4] M $(1, 4)$ •[5] either $x = 3$ or $y = -2$ •[6] B$(3, -2)$

Question			Marking scheme. Give one mark for each •	Max mark	Illustration of evidence for awarding a mark at each •
10.			Ans: $\dfrac{3\sqrt{3}}{2}$ •^{1} start to differentiate •^{2} complete differentiation •^{3} evaluate $f'\left(\dfrac{5\pi}{6}\right)$	3	•^{1} $3 \times 4\sin^2 x$ •^{2} $\times \cos x$ •^{3} $12\left(\dfrac{1}{2}\right)^2 \times \dfrac{-\sqrt{3}}{2} = 12 \times \dfrac{1}{4} \times \dfrac{-\sqrt{3}}{2} = \dfrac{-3\sqrt{3}}{2}$
11.	(a)		•^{1} knows derived function represents gradient and that the minimum value of $f'(x)$ is zero	1	•^{1} $m = f'(x) \geq 0$ stated explicitly
	(b)		•^{2} interprets information correctly •^{3} completes sketch	2	•^{2} stationary point plotted in fourth quadrant •^{3} point of inflexion on an increasing graph
12.	(a)		Ans: $\dfrac{1}{50}$ sec or 0·02 sec •^{1} knows how to find period •^{2} correct answer	2	•^{1} $T = \dfrac{2\pi}{100\pi}$ •^{2} $\dfrac{1}{50}$ or 0·02

Question			Marking scheme. Give one mark for each •	Max mark	Illustration of evidence for awarding a mark at each •
	(b)		Ans: $\dfrac{7}{600}$, $\dfrac{11}{600}$, and $\dfrac{19}{600}$ sec	6	
			•^{1} equating function with -60		•^{1} $120\sin 100\pi t = -60$
			•^{2} rearranging		•^{2} $\sin 100\pi t = -\dfrac{1}{2}$
			•^{3} solve equation for $100\pi t$		•^{3} $100\pi t = \dfrac{7\pi}{6}$ and $\dfrac{11\pi}{6}$
			•^{4} process solutions for t		•^{4} $t = \dfrac{7}{600}$ and $\dfrac{11}{600}$
			•^{5} knowing to use period or demonstrating another solution from the third quadrant		•^{5} $T = \dfrac{1}{50}$ or $100\pi t = 3\pi + \dfrac{\pi}{6}$
			•^{6} third value for t		•^{6} $\dfrac{19}{600}$

HIGHER FOR CfE MATHEMATICS
SPECIMEN QUESTION PAPER

Paper 2

Question		Marking scheme. Give one mark for each •	Max mark	Illustration of evidence for awarding a mark at each •
1.	(a)	•¹ find coordinates of E •² find coordinates of F	2	•¹ E(45, 45, 40) •² F(60, 40, 0)
	(b)	Ans: −1750 •³ find $\overrightarrow{ED}$ and $\overrightarrow{EF}$ •⁴ correct calculation of scalar product	2	•³ $\overrightarrow{ED} = \begin{pmatrix} -15 \\ -15 \\ 40 \end{pmatrix}$, $\overrightarrow{EF} = \begin{pmatrix} 15 \\ -5 \\ -40 \end{pmatrix}$ •⁴ $\overrightarrow{ED}.\overrightarrow{EF} = -225 + 75 - 1600 = -1750$
	(c)	Ans: 154° •⁵ know how to find angle DEF using formula •⁶ find $\lvert\overrightarrow{ED}\rvert$ •⁷ find $\lvert\overrightarrow{EF}\rvert$ •⁸ calculates angle DEF	4	•⁵ $\cos DEF = \dfrac{\overrightarrow{ED}.\overrightarrow{EF}}{\lvert\overrightarrow{ED}\rvert\lvert\overrightarrow{EF}\rvert}$ or equivalent •⁶ $\lvert\overrightarrow{ED}\rvert = \sqrt{2050}$ •⁷ $\lvert\overrightarrow{EF}\rvert = \sqrt{1850}$ •⁸ $\cos DEF = \dfrac{-1750}{\sqrt{2050}\,\sqrt{1850}}$ $DEF = 153 \cdot 977\ldots = 154°$
2.	(a)	Ans: $a = 0 \cdot 96$, $b = 580$ •¹ set up one equation •² set up second equation •³ solve for one variable •⁴ solve for second variable	4	•¹ $2500 = 2000a + b$ •² $2980 = 2500a + b$ •³ $480 = 500a$ or $\quad 12\,500 = 10\,000a + 5b$ $\quad a = \dfrac{480}{500} \qquad 11\,920 = 10\,000a + 4b$ $\qquad\qquad\qquad\qquad 580 = b$ $\quad a = 0 \cdot 96$ •⁴ $b = 2500 - 2000\,(0 \cdot 96)$ $\quad b = 2500 - 1920$ $\quad b = 580$ or $\quad 2000a = 2500 - 580$ $\qquad a = \dfrac{1920}{2000}$ $\qquad a = 0 \cdot 96$

Question		Marking scheme. Give one mark for each •	Max mark	Illustration of evidence for awarding a mark at each •
	(b)	Ans: Yes. Stabilises at 14500	3	
		•^{5} knows how to find the limit		•^{5} $u_{n+1} = 0 \cdot 96 u_n + 580, \quad -1 < a < 1$ $$L = \frac{b}{1-a}$$ $$L = \frac{580}{1-0 \cdot 96}$$
		•^{6} calculate limit		•^{6} $L = 14500$
		•^{7} conclusion		•^{7} yes, conservation measures will end, since the predicted population stabilises at 14500 and 14500 > 13000
3.	(a)	Ans: $p = 1, q = 4$	1	
		•^{1} state values of p and q		•^{1} $p = 1, q = 4$
	(b)	Ans: $y = 9(x-1)$	4	
		•^{2} expand brackets		•^{2} $f(x) = x^4 - 9x^3 + 24x^2 - 16x$
		•^{3} differentiate		•^{3} $f'(x) = 4x^3 - 27x^2 + 48x - 16$
		•^{4} calculate gradient of tangent		•^{4} $f'(1) = 4 - 27 + 48 - 16 = 9$
		•^{5} substitutes gradient and (1,0) into equation of line		•^{5} $y = 9(x-1)$
4.	(a)	Ans: $y = \log_4 x + \dfrac{1}{2}$	2	
		•^{1} using law of logarithms		•^{1} $\log_4 2x = \log_4 2 + \log_4 x$
		•^{2} evaluating $\log_4 2$		•^{2} $\log_4 2 = \dfrac{1}{2}$
	(b)	Ans: Graph of $y = \log_4 x$ moved up by $\dfrac{1}{2}$ or graph of $y = \log_4 x$ compressed horizontally by a factor of 2.	1	
		•^{3} valid description of relationship		•^{3} valid description — see answer
	(c)	Ans: $x = \dfrac{1}{2}$	2	
		•^{4} setting $y = 0$		•^{4} $\log_4 2x = 0$
		•^{5} solving for x		•^{5} $x = \dfrac{1}{2}$

Question	Marking scheme. Give one mark for each •	Max mark	Illustration of evidence for awarding a mark at each •
(d)	Ans: •6 reflecting $y = \log_4 2x$ in the line $y = x$ •7 correct shape •8 annotating (2 points) (or other valid method)	3	•6 reflect in $y = x$ •7 •8 $\left(0, \dfrac{1}{2}\right)$ and $\left(\dfrac{1}{2}, 1\right)$
5. (a)	Ans: $y - 1 = -2(x - 3)$ •1 calculate midpoint of AB •2 calculate gradient of AB •3 state gradient of perpendicular bisector •4 substitute into equation of line	4	•1 (3, 1) •2 $\dfrac{1}{2}$ •3 −2 •4 $y - 1 = -2(x - 3)$
(b)	Ans: $(x - 2)^2 + (y - 3)^2 = 25$ •5 knowing and using $y = 3$ •6 solving for x •7 identifying the radius •8 obtain circle equation	4	•5 $3 = -2x + 7$ •6 $x = 2$ •7 $r = 5$ •8 $(x - 2)^2 + (y - 3)^2 = 25$

Question	Marking scheme. Give one mark for each •	Max mark	Illustration of evidence for awarding a mark at each •
6.	Ans: $x = -3$	5	
	•[1] use perpendicular property		•[1] If $\overrightarrow{CD}$ is perpendicular to $\overrightarrow{AB}$ then $\overrightarrow{CD}.\overrightarrow{AB} = 0$
	•[2] find $\overrightarrow{CD}$		•[2] $\begin{pmatrix} x-4 \\ -3 \\ -1 \end{pmatrix}$
	•[3] find $\overrightarrow{AB}$		•[3] $\begin{pmatrix} 5 \\ -10 \\ -5 \end{pmatrix}$
	•[4] correct substitution into scalar product formula		•[4] $5(x-4)+(-10)(-3)+(-5)(-1) = 0$
	•[5] calculates value of x		•[5] $x = -3$
7.	Ans: A False and B True	6	
	•[1] valid reason for statement A		•[1] $P(0) = 30e^{-2} = 4\cdot06$
	•[2] selecting true or false for statement A with valid reason		•[2] false, since $P(0) \neq 30$ (do not award without valid reason)
	•[3] setting $P(t) = 15$		•[3] $15 = 30e^{t-2}$
	•[4] taking log to base e		•[4] $\ln e^{t-2} = \ln 0\cdot5$
	•[5] completing valid reason		•[5] $t - 2 = \ln 0\cdot5$ $t = \ln 0\cdot5 + 2$ (1·3)
	•[6] selecting true or false for statement B with valid reason		•[6] true, since $t = 1\cdot3$ to one decimal place and there is only one solution (do not award without valid reason)
Notes	Substituting $t = 1\cdot3$ into $P(t) = 30e^{t-2}$ is not sufficient to show that statement B is true, since it does not prove that $t = 13$ is the <u>only</u> solution.		
8. (a)	•[1] know to equate volume to 100	3	•[1] $V = \pi r^2 h = 100$
	•[2] obtain an expression for h		•[2] $h = \dfrac{100}{\pi r^2}$
	•[3] complete area evaluation		•[3] $A = \pi r^2 + 2\pi r^2 + 2\pi r \times \dfrac{100}{\pi r^2}$

Question			Marking scheme. Give one mark for each •	Max mark	Illustration of evidence for awarding a mark at each •
	(b)		Ans: $r = 2 \cdot 20$ m	6	
			•⁴ know to and start to differentiate		•⁴ $A'(r) = 6\pi r ...$
			•⁵ complete differentiation		•⁵ $A'(r) = 6\pi r - \dfrac{200}{r^2}$
			•⁶ set derivative to zero		•⁶ $6\pi r - \dfrac{200}{r^2} = 0$
			•⁷ obtain r		•⁷ $r = 2 \cdot 20$ metres
			•⁸ justify nature of stationary point		•⁸ $A''(r) = 6\pi + \dfrac{400}{r^3} \Rightarrow A''(2\cdot1974...) = 56\cdot5...$
			•⁹ interpret result		•⁹ minimum (when $r = 2\cdot20$ m)
Notes			Candidates may use a nature table at •⁸ to justify a minimum turning point when $r = 2\cdot1974...$		
9.			Ans: $\dfrac{5}{6}$	6	
			•¹ knowing to use integration		•¹ $\displaystyle\int \sin\left(\tfrac{3}{4}x - \tfrac{3}{2}\pi\right)dx - \int \cos(2x)dx$
			•² using correct limits		•² $\displaystyle\int_0^{\frac{3}{2}\pi} \sin\left(\tfrac{3}{4}x - \tfrac{3}{2}\pi\right)dx - \int_0^{\frac{x}{4}} \cos(2x)dx$
			•³ integrating correctly		•³ $\left[-\tfrac{4}{3}\cos(\tfrac{3}{4}x - \tfrac{3}{2}\pi)\right].....$
			•⁴ integrating correctly		•⁴ $-\left[\tfrac{1}{2}\sin(2x)\right]$
			•⁵ substituting limits correctly		•⁵ See * below
			•⁶ evaluating correctly		•⁶ $\left(\tfrac{4}{3} - 0\right) - \left(\tfrac{1}{2} - 0\right) = \tfrac{5}{6}$
			* $\left(\left[-\tfrac{4}{3}\cos\left(\tfrac{3}{4} \times \tfrac{3}{2}\pi - \tfrac{3}{2}\pi\right)\right] - \left[-\tfrac{4}{3}\cos\left(0 - \tfrac{3}{2}\pi\right)\right]\right) - \left(\left[\tfrac{1}{2}\sin\left(2 \times \tfrac{1}{4}\pi\right)\right]\right) - \left[\tfrac{1}{2}\sin(2 \times 0)\right]\right)$		
10.	(a)		Ans: $k = 2,\ \alpha = \dfrac{\pi}{6}$ or equivalent	4	
			•¹ knows to set wave function equal to addition of individual waves		•¹ $\sin t + \sqrt{3}\cos t = k\cos(t - \alpha)$ or equivalent
			•² knows to expand		•² $k\cos\alpha\cos t + k\sin\alpha\sin x$ or equivalent
			•³ knows to compare coefficients		•³ $k\sin\alpha = 1,\quad k\cos\alpha = \sqrt{3}$ or equivalent
			•⁴ interpret comparison		•⁴ $k = 2,\quad \alpha = \dfrac{\pi}{6}$ or equivalent

Question	Marking scheme. Give one mark for each •	Max mark	Illustration of evidence for awarding a mark at each •
(b)	Ans: 5·9 •⁵ equates wave function with y-coordinate of P •⁶ rearranges correctly •⁷ solve equation for $t - \dfrac{\pi}{6}$ •⁸ find t-coordinate of P by interpreting diagram	4	•⁵ $2\cos\left(t - \dfrac{\pi}{6}\right) = 1\cdot2$ or equivalent •⁶ $\cos\left(t - \dfrac{\pi}{6}\right) = 0\cdot6$ or equivalent •⁷ •⁷ $t - \dfrac{\pi}{6} = 0\cdot927...$ & $5\cdot355...$ $1\cdot45...$ & •⁸ $5\cdot879...$

HIGHER FOR CfE MATHEMATICS
MODEL PAPER 1

Paper 1 (Non-Calculator)

Question			Marking scheme. Give one mark for each •	Max mark	Illustration of evidence for awarding a mark at each •
1.			Ans: $2x - y = 5$	3	
			•[1] know to find m_{AB}		•[1] $m_{AB} = \dfrac{7-3}{4-2}$
			•[2] use $m_{DC} = m_{AB}$		•[2] $m_{DC} = 2$
			•[3] find equation of line		•[3] $y - 11 = 2(x - 8)$
2.			Ans: $Q\,(3,1,-2)$	3	
			•[1] interpret ratio		•[1] e.g. $\overrightarrow{PQ} = 2\overrightarrow{QR}$
			•[2] start evaluation of components		•[2] $3\mathbf{q} = 2\begin{pmatrix} 5 \\ 2 \\ -3 \end{pmatrix} + \begin{pmatrix} -1 \\ -1 \\ 0 \end{pmatrix}$
			•[3] complete evaluation of coordinates		•[3] $Q\,(3,1,-2)$
3.			Ans: $k = 24$	4	
			•[1] know discriminant $= 0$		•[1] $b^2 - 4ac = 0$ and $a = k,\ b = k,\ c = 6$ stated or implied by •[2]
			•[2] simplify		•[2] $k^2 - 24k = 0$
			•[3] factorise LHS		•[3] $k(k - 24) = 0$
			•[4] solve for given domain (including rejection of $k = 0$)		•[4] $k = 24$
4.			Ans: $\mathbf{u}.\mathbf{v}=0 \Rightarrow \mathbf{u}$ and $\mathbf{v}$ are perpendicular	2	
			•[1] use scalar product		•[1] $3 \times 2 + 2 \times (-3) + 0 \times 4$
			•[2] communicate solution		•[2] $\mathbf{u}.\mathbf{v}=0 \Rightarrow \mathbf{u}$ and $\mathbf{v}$ are perpendicular
5.			Ans: $2x^2 + \dfrac{1}{x} + c$	4	
			•[1] preparation for integration		•[1] $4x - x^{-2}$
			•[2] correct integration of first term		•[2] $4\dfrac{x^2}{2} - \ldots\ldots$
			•[3] correct integration of second term		•[3] $\ldots\ldots - \dfrac{x^{-1}}{-1}$
			•[4] includes constant of integration		•[4] $2x^2 + x^{-1} + c$
6.	(a)		Ans: $\dfrac{x - 3}{2}$	2	
			•[1] change subject to x		•[1] $y = 2x + 3 \Rightarrow x = \dfrac{y - 3}{2}$
			•[2] express function in terms of x		•[2] $\dfrac{x - 3}{2}$

Question			Marking scheme. Give one mark for each •	Max mark	Illustration of evidence for awarding a mark at each •
	(b)	(i)	Ans: $\dfrac{1}{2x-1}$ •¹ start composite process •² find $h(x)$ in simplest form	2	•¹ e.g. $f(2x+3)$ •² $\dfrac{1}{2x-1}$
		(ii)	Ans: $x \neq \dfrac{1}{2}$ •¹ state restriction	1	•¹ $x \neq \dfrac{1}{2}$
7.			Ans: $g^2+f^2-c=-\dfrac{7}{4}$, so equation does not represent a circle since $g^2+f^2-c<0$ •¹ use g^2+f^2-c •² communicate solution	2	•¹ $g^2+f^2-c=1^2+\left(\dfrac{3}{2}\right)^2-5$ •² $g^2+f^2-c=-\dfrac{7}{4}$, so equation does not represent a circle since $g^2+f^2-c<0$.
8.	(a)		Ans: $9\cdot8\,\text{m/s}$ •¹ know to differentiate •² differentiate correctly •³ find speed after 1 second	3	•¹ $\dfrac{dh}{dt}=\ldots\ldots$ •² $\dfrac{dh}{dt}=19\cdot6-9\cdot8t$ •³ $9\cdot8\,\text{m/s}$
	(b)		Ans: 2 seconds •¹ know how to find stationary point •² communicate solution	2	•¹ e.g. $19\cdot6-9\cdot8t=0$ •² 2 seconds
9.	(a)		Ans: $8-(x+1)^2$ •¹ complete the square •² process for a	2	•¹ $\ldots-(x+1)^2$ •² $8-(x+1)^2$
	(b)		Ans: 8; maximum value occurs when $(x+1)^2=0$. •¹ state maximum value •² justification	2	•¹ 8 •² e.g. maximum value occurs when $(x+1)^2=0$.
10.			Ans: $a=-2$, $b=5$ •¹ use fact that graph of $y=\log_b x$ passes through $(1,0)$ •² state value of a •³ state value of b	3	•¹ graph of $y=\log_b(x+a)$ is graph of $y=\log_b x$ moved 2 units right •² -2 •³ 5

Question			Marking scheme. Give one mark for each •	Max mark	Illustration of evidence for awarding a mark at each •
11.			Ans: •¹ identify roots •² interpret point of inflection •³ complete cubic curve	3	 •¹ 0 and c only •² turning point at $(0,0)$ •³ correct shape
12.	(a)		Ans: $(-1, 4)$ maximum turning point; $(1, 0)$ minimum turning point •¹ differentiate correctly •² set derivative to zero •³ solve for x •⁴ evaluate y-coordinates •⁵ justify nature of stationary points •⁶ interpret result	6	 •¹ $f'(x) = 3x^2 - 3$ •² $3x^2 - 3 = 0$ •³ $x = -1, x = 1$ •⁴ $y = 4, y = 0$ •⁵ $\begin{array}{cccc} x & ..-1.. & & ..1.. \\ f'(x) & +\ 0\ - & & -\ 0+ \end{array}$ •⁶ $(-1, 4)$ max. turning point; $(1, 0)$ min. turning point
	(b)	(i)	Ans: **proof** •¹ know to use $x = 1$ •² complete synthetic division •³ recognition of zero remainder	3	 •¹ $\begin{array}{c|cccc} 1 & 1 & 0 & -3 & 2 \end{array}$ •² $\begin{array}{c|cccc} 1 & 1 & 0 & -3 & 2 \\ & & 0 & 1 & 1 & 2 \\ \hline & 1 & 1 & -2 & 0 \end{array}$ •³ $(x-1)$ is a factor as remainder is zero
		(ii)	Ans: $(x-1)(x-1)(x+2)$ •¹ identify quotient •² factorise fully	2	 •¹ $x^2 + x + 2$ •² $(x-1)(x-1)(x+2)$

Question			Marking scheme. Give one mark for each •	Max mark	Illustration of evidence for awarding a mark at each •
	(c)		Ans: x-axis $(1,0)$ and $(-2,0)$; y-axis $(0,2)$. •^{1} state y-intercepts •^{2} state x-intercepts •^{3} sketch of correct cubic curve with stationary points shown and labelled •^{4} intercepts with axes shown and labelled on sketch	4	•^{1} $(0,2)$ •^{2} $(1,0)$ and $(-2,0)$ •^{3} sketch of correct cubic curve with max. t.p.$(-1,4)$ and min. t.p. $(1,0)$ shown and labelled •^{4} intercepts $(0,2),(1,0)$ and $(-2,0)$ shown and labelled on sketch
13.			Ans: $-\dfrac{3}{5}$ •^{1} express DEA in terms of $x°$ •^{2} expand $\cos(2x+90)°$ •^{3} simplify •^{4} expand $\sin 2x°$ •^{5} find exact length of CE •^{6} substitute into $-2\sin x°\cos x°$ •^{7} find exact value of cos DEA	7	•^{1} $(2x+90)°$ •^{2} $\cos 2x°\cos 90° - \sin 2x°\sin 90°$ •^{3} $-\sin 2x°$ •^{4} $-2\sin x°\cos x°$ •^{5} $\sqrt{10}$ •^{6} $-2 \times \dfrac{1}{\sqrt{10}} \times \dfrac{3}{\sqrt{10}}$ •^{7} $-\dfrac{3}{5}$

HIGHER FOR CfE MATHEMATICS
MODEL PAPER 1

Paper 2

Question			Marking scheme. Give one mark for each •	Max mark	Illustration of evidence for awarding a mark at each •
1.	(a)		Ans: $y = 2x - 5$	4	
			•¹ find midpoint of BC		•¹ $(1, -3)$
			•² find gradient of BC		•² $m_{BC} = -\dfrac{1}{2}$
			•³ find perpendicular gradient		•³ $m_{perp} = 2$
			•⁴ show steps leading to equation of perpendicular bisector in given form		•⁴ $y - (-3) = 2(x - 1)$ $y + 3 = 2x - 2$ $y = 2x - 5$
	(b)		Ans: $3x + y = 10$	3	
			•¹ find midpoint of AB		•¹ $(2, 4)$
			•² find gradient of median		•² $m_{median} = -3$
			•³ find equation of median		•³ $y - (-5) = -3(x - 5)$
	(c)		Ans: $(3, 1)$	3	
			•¹ use valid approach		•¹ e.g. $2x - 5 = -3x + 10$
			•² solve for one variable		•² $x = 3$ or $y = 1$
			•³ find coordinates of point of intersection		•³ $(3, 1)$
2.	(a)		Ans: $\mathbf{B(4, 4, 0)}$	1	
			•¹ state coordinates of B		•¹ $(4, 4, 0)$
	(b)		Ans: $\overrightarrow{DB} = \begin{pmatrix} 2 \\ 2 \\ -6 \end{pmatrix}$, $\overrightarrow{DM} = \begin{pmatrix} 0 \\ -2 \\ -6 \end{pmatrix}$	3	
			•¹ state components of $\overrightarrow{DB}$		•¹ $\begin{pmatrix} 2 \\ 2 \\ -6 \end{pmatrix}$
			•² find coordinates of M		•² $(2, 0, 0)$ stated or implied by •³
			•³ state components of $\overrightarrow{DM}$		•³ $\begin{pmatrix} 0 \\ -2 \\ -6 \end{pmatrix}$
	(c)		Ans: $40 \cdot 3°$ or $0 \cdot 703$ rads	5	
			•¹ know to use scalar product		•¹ $\cos BDM = \dfrac{\overrightarrow{DB}.\overrightarrow{DM}}{|\overrightarrow{DB}||\overrightarrow{DM}|}$
			•² find scalar product		•² $\overrightarrow{DB}.\overrightarrow{DM} = 32$
			•³ find magnitude of a vector		•³ $|\overrightarrow{DB}| = \sqrt{44}$
			•⁴ find magnitude of a vector		•⁴ $|\overrightarrow{DM}| = \sqrt{40}$
			•⁵ evaluate angle BDM		•⁵ $40 \cdot 3°$ or $0 \cdot 703$ rads

Question			Marking scheme. Give one mark for each •	Max mark	Illustration of evidence for awarding a mark at each •
3.	(a)		Ans: 2·5 metres	3	
			•[1] use recurrence relation		•[1] $u_{n+1} = 0\cdot8u_n + 0\cdot5$
			•[2] know how to find limit		•[2] $L = \dfrac{0\cdot5}{1-0\cdot8}$
			•[3] calculate limit		•[3] 2·5 metres
	(b)		Ans: 25%	3	
			•[1] set up equation involving limit		•[1] $\dfrac{0\cdot5}{1-b} = 2$
			•[2] solve equation		•[2] $b = 0\cdot75$
			•[3] state percentage		•[3] 25%
4.			Ans: $21\dfrac{1}{12}$ or $\dfrac{253}{12}$ or $21\cdot1$	10	
			•[1] know to integrate		•[1] $\int \ldots$ or attempt integration
			•[2] know to deal with areas on each side of y-axis		•[2] evidence of attempting to interpret the diagram to left of y-axis separately from diagram to right
			•[3] interpret limits of one area		•[3] e.g. $\displaystyle\int_{-2}^{0}$
			•[4] use "upper − lower"		•[4] $(x^3 - x^2 - 4x + 4) - (2x + 4)$
			•[5] integrate		•[5] $\dfrac{1}{4}x^4 - \dfrac{1}{3}x^3 - 3x^2$
			•[6] substitute in limits		•[6] $-(\dfrac{1}{4}(-2)^4 - \dfrac{1}{3}(-2)^3 - 3(-2)^2)$ Evidence for •[6] may be implied by •[7] but •[7] must be consistent with •[5]
			•[7] evaluate the area on one side		•[7] $\dfrac{16}{3}$
			•[8] interpret integrand with the limits of the other area		•[8] $\displaystyle\int_{0}^{3} (2x - 4) - (x^3 - x^2 - 4x + 4)dx$
			•[9] evaluate the area on the other side		•[9] $\dfrac{63}{4}$
			•[10] state total area		•[10] $21\dfrac{1}{12}$ or $\dfrac{253}{12}$ or $21\cdot1$
5.	(a)		Ans: $k = 13$, $a = 22\cdot6$	4	
			•[1] use addition formula		•[1] $k\cos x° \cos a° - k\sin° x \sin a°$ or $k(\cos x° \cos a° - \sin° \sin a°)$
			•[2] compare coefficients		•[2] $k\cos a° = 12$ **and** $k\sin a° = 5$ or $-k\sin a° = -5$
			•[3] process k		•[3] 13
			•[4] process a		•[4] $22\cdot6$

Question			Marking scheme. Give one mark for each •	Max mark	Illustration of evidence for awarding a mark at each •
	(b)	(i)	Ans: max. = 13, min. = −13	1	
			•¹ state maximum and minimum		•¹ 13, −13
		(ii)	Ans: max. at 337·4, min. at 157·4	2	
			•¹ find x corresponding to maximum value		•¹ maximum at 337·4
			•² find x corresponding to minimum value		•² minimum at 157·4
6.			Ans: 0·363	4	
			•¹ start to integrate		•¹ $-\cos(4x + 1)$
			•² complete integration		•² $-\dfrac{1}{4}\cos(4x + 1)$
			•³ substitute in limits		•³ $-\dfrac{1}{4}\cos 9 - (-\dfrac{1}{4}\cos 1)$
			•⁴ evaluate integral		•⁴ 0·363
7.	(a)	(i)	Ans: proof	4	**Method 1**
			•¹ substitute		•¹ $x^2 + (3 - x)^2 + 14x + 4(3 - x) - 19 = 0$
			•² express in standard form		•² $2x^2 + 4x + 2 = 0$
			•³ start proof		•³ $2(x + 1)(x + 1) = 0$
			•⁴ complete proof		•⁴ equal roots so line is a tangent
					Method 2
					•¹ $x^2 + (3 - x)^2 + 14x + 4(3 - x) - 19 = 0$
					•² $2x^2 + 4x + 2 = 0$
					•³ $b^2 - 4ac = 4^2 - 4 \times 2 \times 2$
					•⁴ $b^2 - 4ac = 0$ so line is a tangent
		(ii)	Ans: (−1, 4)	1	
			•¹ state coordinates of P		•¹ (−1, 4)

Question			Marking scheme. Give one mark for each •	Max mark	Illustration of evidence for awarding a mark at each •
7.	(b)		Ans: $(x-1)^2 + (y-6)^2 = 8$ or $x^2 + y^2 - 2x - 12y = 29 = 0$	6	
			Method 1		**Method 1**
			•¹ state centre of larger circle		•¹ $(-7, -2)$
			•² find radius of larger circle		•² $\sqrt{72}$
			•³ find radius of smaller circle		•³ $\sqrt{8}$
			•⁴ strategy for finding centre		•⁴ e.g. "stepping out"
			•⁵ interpret centre of smaller circle		•⁵ $(1,6)$
			•⁶ state equation		•⁶ $(x-1)^2 + (y-6)^2 = 8$ or $x^2 + y^2 - 2x - 12y = 29 = 0$
			Method 2		**Method 2**
			•¹ state centre of larger circle		•¹ $(-7, -2)$
			•² strategy for finding centre		•² e.g. "stepping out"
			•³ state centre of smaller circle		•³ $(1,6)$
			•⁴ strategy for finding radius		•⁴ $\sqrt{2^2 + 2^2}$
			•⁵ find radius of smaller circle		•⁵ $\sqrt{8}$
			•⁶ state equation		•⁶ $(x-1)^2 + (y-6)^2 = 8$ or $x^2 + y^2 - 2x - 12y = 29 = 0$
8.	(a)		Ans: 4433 micrograms	3	
			•¹ interpret equation		•¹ $600 = A_0 e^{-0.002 \times 1000}$
			•² process equation		•² $A_0 = \dfrac{600}{e^{-0.002 \times 1000}}$
			•³ process for A_0		•³ $A_0 \approx 4433$ micrograms
	(b)		Ans: 346·6 years	5	
			•¹ interpret half-life		•¹ $\frac{1}{2}A_0 = A_0 e^{-0.002t}$
			•² process equation		•² $e^{-0.002t} = \dfrac{1}{2}$
			•³ take log to base e		•³ $\ln e^{-0.002t} = \ln \dfrac{1}{2}$
			•⁴ process log equation		•⁴ $t = \dfrac{\log_e \frac{1}{2}}{-0.002}$
			•⁵ process for t		•⁵ 346·6 years

Question			Marking scheme. Give one mark for each •	Max mark	Illustration of evidence for awarding a mark at each •
9.			Ans: 2·419, 3·864 and no solution	5	
			•^{1} use double angle formula		•^{1} $2 \times (2\cos^2 x - 1)......$
			•^{2} express as quadratic in $\cos x$		•^{2} $4\cos^2 x - 5\cos x - 6 = 0$
			•^{3} start to solve		•^{3} $(4\cos x + 3)(\cos x - 2) = 0$ or $\cos x = \dfrac{(-5)^2 \pm \sqrt{4 \times 4 \times (-6)}}{2 \times 4}$
			•^{4} solve for $\cos x$		•^{4} $\cos x = -\dfrac{3}{4}$ and $\cos x = 2$
			•^{5} solve for x		•^{5} 2·419, 3·864 and no solution

HIGHER FOR CfE MATHEMATICS
MODEL PAPER 2

Paper 1 (Non-Calculator)

Question			Marking scheme. Give one mark for each •	Max mark	Illustration of evidence for awarding a mark at each •
1.	(a)		Ans: $2x - y = 1$ •¹ find midpoint of AC •² find gradient of median •³ find equation of median	3	 •¹ $(3,5)$ •² $m_{median} = 2$ •³ $y - (-5) = 2(x - (-2))$
	(b)		Ans: $3x + y = 9$ •¹ find gradient of BC •² find perpendicular gradient •³ find equation of altitude	3	 •¹ $m_{BC} = \dfrac{1}{3}$ •² $m_{perp} = -3$ •³ $y - 12 = -3(x - (-1))$
	(c)		Ans: $(2,3)$ •¹ use valid approach •² solve for one variable •³ find coordinates of point of intersection	3	 •¹ e.g. $2x - 1 = -3x + 9$ •² $x = 2$ or $y = 3$ •³ $(2,3)$
2.			Ans: $C(7,7,8)$ •¹ set up vector equation •² express **c** in terms of **a** and **b** •³ evaluate components •⁴ state coordinates	4	 •¹ c-b=2(b-a) •² c=3b-2a •³ $\mathbf{c} = 3\begin{pmatrix}1\\3\\2\end{pmatrix} - 2\begin{pmatrix}-2\\1\\-1\end{pmatrix}$ •⁴ C(7,7,8)
3.	(a)		Ans: $\dfrac{1}{\sqrt{2}}$ •¹ use addition formula •² find exact length of hypotenuse in each triangle •³ substitute into expansion •⁴ evaluate exact value of $\sin(c + d)$	4	 •¹ $\sin c \cos d + \cos c \sin d$ •² $\sqrt{5}$ and $\sqrt{10}$ •³ $\dfrac{1}{\sqrt{5}} \times \dfrac{3}{\sqrt{10}} + \dfrac{2}{\sqrt{5}} \times \dfrac{1}{\sqrt{10}}$ •⁴ $\dfrac{5}{\sqrt{50}}$
	(b)	(i)	Ans: $\dfrac{4}{5}$ •¹ use double angle formula •² evaluate exact value of $\sin 2c$	2	 •¹ $2\sin c \cos c = 2 \times \dfrac{1}{\sqrt{5}} \times \dfrac{2}{\sqrt{5}}$ •² $\dfrac{4}{5}$

Question			Marking scheme. Give one mark for each •	Max mark	Illustration of evidence for awarding a mark at each •
		(ii)	Ans: proof	2	
			•[1] use double angle formula		•[1] $\cos^2 d - \sin^2 d = (\frac{3}{\sqrt{10}})^2 - (\frac{1}{\sqrt{10}})^2$
			•[2] complete steps leading to exact value of $\cos 2d$		•[2] $\frac{9}{10} - \frac{1}{10} = \frac{8}{10} = \frac{4}{5}$
4.			Ans: $a = 4$, $b = 2$, $c = 1$	3	
			•[1] state value of a		•[1] 4
			•[2] state value of b		•[2] 2
			•[3] state value of c		•[3] 1
5.	(a)		Ans: $1\frac{1}{4}$ units^2	4	
			•[1] know to integrate		•[1] $\int_0^1 x^3 - 6x^2 + 4x + 1 \, dx$
			•[2] integrate		•[2] $\left[\frac{1}{4}x^4 - 2x^3 + 2x^2 + x\right]_0^1$
			•[3] substitute in limits		•[3] $\frac{1}{4}(1)^4 - 2(1)^3 + 2(1)^2 + 1$
			•[4] evaluate area		•[4] $1\frac{1}{4}$
	(b)		Ans: $4\frac{1}{2}$ units^2	3	
			•[1] know how to find area below x-axis		•[1] $-\int_1^2 x^3 - 6x^2 + 4x + 1 \, dx$
			•[2] integrate and substitute in limits		•[2] $-((\frac{1}{4}(2)^4 - 2(2)^3 + 2(2)^2 + 2) - 1\frac{1}{4})$
			•[3] evaluate total area		•[3] $4\frac{1}{2}$
6.			**Ans: proof**	5	
			•[1] set equation of parabola equal to equation of line		•[1] $x^2 + 3x + 4 = 2x + 1$
			•[2] express in standard form		•[2] $x^2 + x + 3 = 0$
			•[3] start proof		•[3] $b^2 - 4ac = 1^2 - 4 \times 1 \times 3$
			•[4] continue proof		•[4] $b^2 - 4ac = -11$ $b^2 - 4ac < 0 \Rightarrow$ no real roots
			•[5] communication		•[5] no real roots $\Rightarrow$ line and parabola do not intersect

Question			Marking scheme. Give one mark for each •	Max mark	Illustration of evidence for awarding a mark at each •
7.			Ans: $\dfrac{2}{3}$	4	
			•¹ preparation for integration		•¹ $\displaystyle\int_0^1 (3x+1)^{-\frac{1}{2}}\, dx$
			•² integrate		•² $\dfrac{(3x+1)^{\frac{1}{2}}}{3 \times \frac{1}{2}}$
			•³ substitute in limits		•³ $\dfrac{4^{\frac{1}{2}}}{3 \times \frac{1}{2}} - \dfrac{1^{\frac{1}{2}}}{3 \times \frac{1}{2}}$
			•⁴ evaluate integral		•⁴ $\dfrac{2}{3}$
8.			Ans: $x < -2$ and $x > 3$	4	
			•¹ differentiate		•¹ $f'(x) = 6x^2 - 6x - 36$
			•² know that $f'(x) > 0$		•² $6x^2 - 6x - 36 > 0$
			•³ factorise		•³ $6(x+2)(x-3) > 0$
			•⁴ correct range		•⁴ $x < -2$ and and $x > 3$
9.			Ans: 2	3	
			•¹ use law of logarithms		•¹ $\log_5 2 + \log_5 50 = \log_5 100$
			•² use law of logarithms		•² $\log_5 100 - \log_5 4 = \log_5 25$
			•³ evaluate logarithm		•³ $\log_5 25 = 2$
10.			Ans: $\dfrac{\pi}{18}, \dfrac{5\pi}{18}, \dfrac{13\pi}{18}, \dfrac{17\pi}{18}$	4	
			•¹ solve for $\sin 3x$		•¹ $\sin 3x = \dfrac{1}{2}$
			•² solve for $0 \le 3x \le \pi$		•² $3x = \dfrac{\pi}{18}, \dfrac{5\pi}{6}$
			•³ solve for $\pi \le 3x \le 3\pi$		•³ $3x = \dfrac{13\pi}{6}, \dfrac{17\pi}{6}$
			•⁴ solve for $0 \le x \le \pi$		•⁴ $3x = \dfrac{\pi}{18}, \dfrac{5\pi}{18}, \dfrac{13\pi}{18}, \dfrac{17\pi}{18}$
11.			Ans: $\sqrt{37}$	4	
			•¹ centre of smaller circle		•¹ $(3,4)$
			•² use general equation of circle to determine value of k		•² $k = 6$
			•³ use $r = \sqrt{g^2 + f^2 - c}$		•³ $r = \sqrt{(-3)^2 + (-4)^2 + 12}$
			•⁴ find radius of larger circle		•⁴ $\sqrt{37}$, since $\sqrt{37} > 5$

Question	Marking scheme. Give one mark for each •	Max mark	Illustration of evidence for awarding a mark at each •
12. (a)	Ans: •¹ scale parallel to x-axis •² annotate graph	2	•¹ sketch and one point correct •² other two points correct
(b)	Ans: •¹ correct order for reflection and translation •² start to annotate final sketch •³ complete annotation	3	•¹ reflect in x-axis, then vertical translation •² sketch and one final point correct •³ the other two final points correct

HIGHER FOR CfE MATHEMATICS
MODEL PAPER 2

Paper 2

Question			Marking scheme. Give one mark for each •	Max mark	Illustration of evidence for awarding a mark at each •
1.	(a)		Ans: M(0,1,0), N(4,2,2) •¹ find coordinates of M •² find coordinates of N	2	•¹ (0,1,0) •² (4,2,2)
	(b)		Ans: $\overrightarrow{VM} = \begin{pmatrix} 0 \\ -1 \\ -3 \end{pmatrix}$, $\overrightarrow{VN} = \begin{pmatrix} 4 \\ 0 \\ -1 \end{pmatrix}$ •¹ express $\overrightarrow{VM}$ in component form •² express $\overrightarrow{VN}$ in component form	2	•¹ $\begin{pmatrix} 0 \\ -1 \\ -3 \end{pmatrix}$ •² $\begin{pmatrix} 4 \\ 0 \\ -1 \end{pmatrix}$
	(c)		Ans: $76 \cdot 7°$ or $1 \cdot 339$ rads •¹ know to use scalar product •² find scalar product •³ find magnitude of a vector •⁴ find magnitude of a vector •⁵ evaluate angle BDM	5	•¹ $\cos MVN = \dfrac{\overrightarrow{VM}.\overrightarrow{VN}}{\left|\overrightarrow{VM}\right|\left|\overrightarrow{VN}\right|}$ •² $\overrightarrow{VM}.\overrightarrow{VN} = 3$ •³ $\left|\overrightarrow{VM}\right| = \sqrt{10}$ •⁴ $\left|\overrightarrow{VN}\right| = \sqrt{17}$ •⁵ $76 \cdot 7°$ or $1 \cdot 339$ rads
2.	(a)		Ans: $k = -5$ •¹ start synthetic division •² complete synthetic division •³ find valu e of k	3	•¹ $-2\underline{\begin{array}{rrrr} 2 & 1 & k & 2 \end{array}}$ •² $-2\underline{\begin{array}{rrrr} 2 & 1 & k & 2 \\ & -4 & 6 & -2k-12 \end{array}}$ $\quad\quad 2 \quad 3 \quad k+6 \;\; -2k-10$ •³ $k = -5$
	(b)		Ans: $x = -2, \dfrac{1}{2}, 1$ •¹ start to factorise •² complete factorisation and solve equation	2	•¹ $(x+2)(2x^2 - 3x + 1)$ •² $(x+2)(2x-1)(x-1) = 0$ $\Rightarrow x = -2, \dfrac{1}{2}, 1$
3.			Ans: $\dfrac{dy}{dx} = 3\cos x - 2\sin 2x$ •¹ differentiate first term •² start to differentiate second term •³ complete differentiation	3	•¹ $3\cos x$ •² $-\sin 2x$ •³ $3\cos x - 2\sin 2x$

Question			Marking scheme. Give one mark for each •	Max mark	Illustration of evidence for awarding a mark at each •
4.	(a)		Ans: x	3	
			•^{1} start composite process		•^{1} $f(\dfrac{1}{x} - 2)$
			•^{2} substitute in $g(x)$		•^{2} $\dfrac{1}{\dfrac{1}{x} - 2 + 2}$
			•^{3} find $f(g(x))$ in simplest form		•^{3} x
	(b)		Ans: $\sqrt{2x+1}$	3	
			•^{1} start to change subject to x		•^{1} $y = \dfrac{x^2-1}{2} \Rightarrow x^2 - 1 = 2y$
			•^{2} complete changing subject to x		•^{2} $x = \sqrt{2y+1}$
			•^{3} express function in terms of x		•^{3} $\sqrt{2x+1}$
5.			Ans: $y = 2x^2 - 2x^3 + 5$	4	
			•^{1} know to integrate		•^{1} $y = \int 4x - 6x^2 \, dx$
			•^{2} integrate		•^{2} $y = 2x^2 - 2x^3 + c$
			•^{3} substitute in coordinates		•^{3} $9 = 2(-1)^2 - 2(-1)^3 + c$
			•^{4} express y in terms of x		•^{4} $y = 2x^2 - 2x^3 + 5$
6.	(a)		Ans: $u_{n+1} = 1 \cdot 015u_n - 300$	2	
			•^{1} start recurrence relation		•^{1} $u_{n+1} = 1 \cdot 015u_n \ldots \ldots$
			•^{2} complete recurrence relation		•^{2} $u_{n+1} = \ldots \ldots - 300$
	(b)		Ans: 1st December, £290·68	4	
			•^{1} state u_0 and u_1		•^{1} $u_0 = 2500$, $u_1 = 2237 \cdot 5$
			•^{2} find last positive and first negative term		•^{2} $u_8 = 286 \cdot 38$, $u_9 = -9 \cdot 32$
			•^{3} state date of final payment		•^{3} 1st December
			•^{4} state amount of final payment		•^{4} £290·68
7.	(a)		Ans: proof	4	
			•^{1} find midpoint of AB		•^{1} $(3,2)$
			•^{2} find gradient of AB		•^{2} $m_{AB} = 1$
			•^{3} find perpendicular gradient		•^{3} $m_{perp} = -1$
			•^{4} show steps leading to equation of perpendicular bisector in given form		•^{4} $y - 2 = -(x - 3)$ $y - 2 = -x + 3$ $x + y = 5$
	(b)		Ans: $3x - y = 3$	4	
			•^{1} rearrange equation of tangent into the form $y = mx + c$		•^{1} $y = -\dfrac{1}{3}x - \dfrac{1}{3}$
			•^{2} gradient of tangent		•^{2} $m_{tangent} = -\dfrac{1}{3}$
			•^{3} gradient of radius		•^{3} $m_{CA} = 3$
			•^{4} equation of radius		•^{4} $y - 0 = 3(x - 1)$

Question			Marking scheme. Give one mark for each •	Max mark	Illustration of evidence for awarding a mark at each •
	(c)	(i)	Ans: (2, 3) •¹ use valid approach •² find coordinates of centre of circle	2	•¹ e.g. $x + y = 5$ $3x - y = 3$ $\Rightarrow 4x = 8$ •² (2, 3)
		(ii)	Ans: $(x-2)^2 + (y-3)^2 = 10$ •¹ find radius •² state equation of circle	2	•¹ $\sqrt{(2-1)^2 + (3-0)^2} = \sqrt{10}$ •² $(x-2)^2 + (y-3)^2 = 10$
8.	(a)		Ans: $k = \sqrt{34}, a = 59$ $\sqrt{34}\cos(x-59°)$ •¹ use addition formula •² compare coefficients •³ process k •⁴ process a	4	•¹ $k\cos x° \cos a° + k\sin x° \sin a°$ or $k(\cos x° \cos a° + \sin x° \sin a°)$ •² $k\cos a° = 3$ and $k\sin a° = 5$ •³ $\sqrt{34}$ •⁴ 59
	(b)		Ans: $12\cdot3°$ •¹ equate wave function with 4 •² solve for $\cos(x-59)°$ •³ solve for $0 \le x \le 90$	3	•¹ $\sqrt{34}\cos(x-59)° = 4$ •² $\cos(x-59)° = \dfrac{4}{\sqrt{34}}$ •³ $12\cdot3°$

Question			Marking scheme. Give one mark for each •	Max mark	Illustration of evidence for awarding a mark at each •
9.			Ans: $k = 32$, $n = \dfrac{1}{2}$	5	
			Method 1		**Method 1**
			•^{1} introduce logarithms to $y = kx^n$		•^{1} $\log_2 y = \log_2 kx^n$ *stated explicitly*
			•^{2} use laws of logarithms		•^{2} $\log_2 y = n\log_2 x + \log_2 k$ *stated explicitly*
			•^{3} interpret intercept		•^{3} $\log_2 k = 5$ or $\log_2 y = 5$
			•^{4} solve for k		•^{4} $k = 32$ or 2^5
			•^{5} interpret gradient		•^{5} $n = \dfrac{1}{2}$
			Method 2		**Method 2**
			•^{1} state linear equation		•^{1} $\log_2 y = \dfrac{1}{2}\log_2 x + 5$
			•^{2} introduce logarithms		•^{2} $.... + 5\log_2 2$ *or* $.... + \log_2 2^5$
			•^{3} use laws of logarithms		•^{3} $\log_2 y = \log_2 x^{\frac{1}{2}} + ...$
			•^{4} use laws of logarithms		•^{4} $\log_2 y = \log_2 2^5 x^{\frac{1}{2}}$ or $\log_2 y = \log_2 32x^{\frac{1}{2}}$
			•^{5} interpret result		•^{5} $y = 2^5 x^{\frac{1}{2}}$ or $y = 32x^{\frac{1}{2}}$
10.	(a)		Ans: £252 million	1	
			•^{1} state value of ship at launch		•^{1} £252 million
	(b)		Ans: 40 years	4	
			•^{1} interpret equation		•^{1} $252e^{-0.06335t} = 20$
			•^{2} process equation		•^{2} $e^{-0.06335t} = \dfrac{20}{252}$
			•^{3} take log to base e		•^{3} $-0.06335t = \ln\left(\dfrac{20}{252}\right)$
			•^{4} process for t		•^{4} $t = \dfrac{\ln\left(\dfrac{20}{252}\right)}{-0.06335} = 40$ years
11.	(a)		Ans: proof	3	
			•^{1} form equation for surface area		•^{1} $12 = 6xh + 2x^2$
			•^{2} change subject to h		•^{2} $h = \dfrac{6 - x^2}{3x}$
			•^{3} show steps leading to given formula for volume		•^{3} $V(x) = x(2x)\left(\dfrac{6 - x^2}{3x}\right)$ $= \dfrac{2}{3}x(6 - x^2)$

Question		Marking scheme. Give one mark for each •	Max mark	Illustration of evidence for awarding a mark at each •
	(b)	Ans: $x = \sqrt{2}$	5	
		•^{1} prepare for differentiation		•^{1} $V(x) = 4x - \dfrac{2}{3}x^3$
		•^{2} differentiate		•^{2} $V'(x) = 4 - 2x^2$
		•^{3} set derivative equal to 0		•^{3} $4 - 2x^2 = 0$
		•^{4} solve for valid exact value for x		•^{4} $\sqrt{2}$
		•^{5} justify nature of stationary points		•^{5} $\begin{array}{c c} x & ..\sqrt{2}.. \\ V'(x) & +\ 0\ - \end{array}$

HIGHER FOR CfE MATHEMATICS
MODEL PAPER 3

Paper 1 (Non-Calculator)

Question			Marking scheme. Give one mark for each •	Max mark	Illustration of evidence for awarding a mark at each •
1.			Ans: $\sqrt{3}x - y + 2\sqrt{3} = 0$ •^{1} know how to find m_{ST} •^{2} find m_{ST} •^{3} find equation of line	3	•^{1} $m_{ST} = \tan 60°$ •^{2} $m_{ST} = \sqrt{3}$ •^{3} $y - 0 = \sqrt{3}(x - (-2))$
2.			Ans: $\begin{pmatrix} -5 \\ -5 \\ 7 \end{pmatrix}$ •^{1} identify sum of directed line segments equal to $\overrightarrow{CV}$ •^{2} substitute in components •^{3} evaluate $\overrightarrow{CV}$ in component form	3	•^{1} e.g. $\overrightarrow{CV} = \overrightarrow{CB} + \overrightarrow{BA} + \overrightarrow{AV}$ •^{2} $\begin{pmatrix} 2 \\ -10 \\ 2 \end{pmatrix} + \begin{pmatrix} -8 \\ -2 \\ -2 \end{pmatrix} + \begin{pmatrix} 1 \\ 7 \\ 7 \end{pmatrix}$ •^{3} $\begin{pmatrix} -5 \\ -5 \\ 7 \end{pmatrix}$
3.			Ans: $\dfrac{3}{4}$ •^{1} prepare to differentiate •^{2} differentiate •^{3} evaluate derivative	3	•^{1} $f(x) = 3x^{\frac{1}{2}}$ •^{2} $f'(x) = \dfrac{3}{2}x^{-\frac{1}{2}}$ •^{3} $f'(4) = \dfrac{3}{2} \times \dfrac{1}{\sqrt{4}} = \dfrac{3}{4}$
4.			Ans: $2(x + 1)^2 - 5$ •^{1} identify common factor •^{2} complete the square •^{3} process for c	3	•^{1} $2(x^2 + 2x$..... stated or implied by •^{3} •^{2} $2(x + 1)^2$ ..... •^{3} $2(x + 1)^2 - 5$
5.	(a)		Ans: $-2x^2 - 1$ •^{1} start composite process •^{2} find $g(f(x))$ in simplest form	2	•^{1} e.g. $g(x^2 + 1)$ •^{2} $-2x^2 - 1$
	(b)		Ans: $4x - 1$ •^{1} start composite process •^{2} find $g(g(x))$ in simplest form	2	•^{1} e.g. $g(1 - 2x)$ •^{2} $4x - 1$

Question			Marking scheme. Give one mark for each •	Max mark	Illustration of evidence for awarding a mark at each •
6.	(a)		Ans: •¹ reflect in y-axis •² annotate graph	2	•¹ sketch and one point correct •² other three points correct
	(b)		Ans: •¹ scale parallel to y-axis •² annotate graph	2	•¹ sketch and one point correct •² other three points correct
7.			Ans: proof •¹ use addition formula •² substitute in any two values •³ complete proof	3	•¹ $\cos x° \cos 30° - \sin x° \sin 30°$ •² e.g. $\dfrac{3}{5} \times \cos 30° - \dfrac{4}{5} \times \sin 30°$ •³ $\dfrac{3}{5} \times \dfrac{\sqrt{3}}{2} - \dfrac{4}{5} \times \dfrac{1}{2} = \dfrac{3\sqrt{3} - 4}{10}$
8.	(a)		Ans: $u_1 = 8, u_2 = -4$ •¹ find terms of sequence	1	•¹ $u_1 = 8, u_2 = -4$
	(b)		Ans: $p = 2, q = -3$ •¹ interpret sequence •² solve for one variable •³ state second variable	3	•¹ $4p + q = 5$ **and** $5p + q = 7$ •² $p = 2$ or $q = -3$ •³ $q = -3$ or $p = 2$

Question			Marking scheme. Give one mark for each •	Max mark	Illustration of evidence for awarding a mark at each •
	(c)	(i)	Ans: limit for (a) = 0 •^{1} identify which sequence has a limit •^{2} calculate limit	2	•^{1} (a) •^{2} 0
		(ii)	Ans: (b) has no limit since p is outside the interval $-1 < p < 1$ •^{1} explain why other sequence has no limit	1	•^{1} (b) has no limit since p is outside the interval $-1 < p < 1$
9.	(a)	(i)	Ans: **proof** •^{1} know and use $f(a) = 0 \Leftrightarrow a$ is a root	1	•^{1} $f(1) = 1 + 8 + 11 + 20 = 0$ so $x = 1$ is a root
		(ii)	Ans: $(x-1)(x+4)(x+5)$ •^{1} start to find quadratic factor •^{2} complete quadratic factor •^{3} factorise fully	3	•^{1} $(x-1)(x^2\ldots\ldots\ldots\ldots)$ •^{2} $(x^2 + 9x + 20)$ •^{3} $(x-1)(x+4)(x+5)$
	(b)		Ans: $x = 1$ only •^{1} use law of logarithms •^{2} convert to exponential form •^{3} write cubic in standard form •^{4} solve cubic •^{5} interpret valid solution	5	•^{1} $\log_2(x+3)(x^2+5x-4)$ •^{2} $(x+3)(x^2+5x-4) = 2^3$ •^{3} $x^3 + 8x^2 + 11x - 20 = 0$ •^{4} $x = 1$ or $x = -4$ or $x = -5$ •^{5} $x = 1$ only
10.			Ans: $y = \dfrac{7}{6} - \dfrac{1}{3}\cos 3x$ •^{1} know to integrate •^{2} integrate •^{3} substitute in coordinates •^{4} express y in terms of x	4	•^{1} $y = \int \sin 3x \, dx$ •^{2} $y = -\dfrac{1}{3}\cos 3x + c$ •^{3} $1 = -\dfrac{1}{3}\cos(3 \times \dfrac{\pi}{9}) + c$ •^{4} $y = \dfrac{7}{6} - \dfrac{1}{3}\cos 3x$

Question			Marking scheme. Give one mark for each •	Max mark	Illustration of evidence for awarding a mark at each •
11.	(a)		Ans: $2\sin(x-\dfrac{\pi}{3})$	4	
			•^{1} use addition formula		•^{1} $k\sin x^\circ\cos a^\circ - k\cos x^\circ\sin a^\circ$ or $k(\sin x^\circ\cos a^\circ - \cos x^\circ\sin a^\circ)$
			•^{2} compare coefficients		•^{2} $k\cos a^\circ = 1$ **and** $k\sin a^\circ = \sqrt{3}$ or $-k\sin a^\circ = -\sqrt{3}$
			•^{3} process k		•^{3} 2
			•^{4} process a		•^{4} $\dfrac{\pi}{3}$
	(b)		Ans:	5	
			•^{1} sine curve with amplitude 2		•^{1} sketch of sine curve showing amplitude 2
			•^{2} sine curve with vertical translation of 3		•^{2} sketch of sine curve showing vertical translation of 3
			•^{3} sine curve with horizontal translation of $\dfrac{\pi}{3}$		•^{3} sketch of sine curve showing horizontal translation of $\dfrac{\pi}{3}$
			•^{4} start to annotate sketch		•^{4} maximum t.p. $(\dfrac{5\pi}{6}, 5)$ and minimum t.p. $(\dfrac{11\pi}{6}, 1)$
			•^{5} complete annotation		•^{5} end points $(0, 3-\sqrt{3})$ and $(2\pi, 3-\sqrt{3})$
12.			Ans: 13·5	4	
			•^{1} use distributive law		•^{1} a.a+a.b+a.c
			•^{2} process scalar product		•^{2} any one of a.a=9, a.b=0, a.c=4·5
			•^{3} process scalar product		•^{3} another one of a.a=9, a.b=0, a.c=4·5
			•^{4} process scalar product		•^{4} a.(a+b+c)=13·5

Question	Marking scheme. Give one mark for each •	Max mark	Illustration of evidence for awarding a mark at each •
13.	Ans: **proof** •¹ prepare to differentiate •² differentiate •³ interpret derivative •⁴ communicate conclusion	4	•¹ $f(x) = (x+1)^{-1}$ •² $f'(x) = -(x+1)^{-2}$ •³ $f'(x) = \dfrac{-1}{(1+x)^2} \Rightarrow f'(x) < 0$ since $(x+1)^2 > 0$ for all x except $x = -1$ •⁴ $f'(x) < 0 \Rightarrow f(x)$ is decreasing for all values of x except $x = -1$

HIGHER FOR CfE MATHEMATICS
MODEL PAPER 3

Paper 2

Question			Marking scheme. Give one mark for each •	Max mark	Illustration of evidence for awarding a mark at each •
1.	(a)	(i)	Ans: proof	3	
			•[1] use vector approach		•[1] $\overrightarrow{AT} = \begin{pmatrix} 10 \\ 10 \\ 4 \end{pmatrix}$ or $\overrightarrow{TB} = \begin{pmatrix} 15 \\ 15 \\ 6 \end{pmatrix}$
			•[2] compare two vectors		•[2] $\overrightarrow{AT}$ and $\overrightarrow{TB}$ and $\overrightarrow{AT} = \frac{2}{3}\overrightarrow{TB}$ or equivalent
			•[3] complete proof		•[3] $\overrightarrow{AT}$ and $\overrightarrow{TB}$ are parallel and since T is a common point, A, T and B are collinear.
		(ii)	Ans: **2 : 3**	1	
			•[1] state ratio		•[1] **2 : 3**
	(b)		Ans: (7,0,0)	5	
			•[1] interpret C		•[1] (7,0,0)
			•[2] use vector approach		•[2] $\overrightarrow{TC} = \begin{pmatrix} c-3 \\ -2 \\ -3 \end{pmatrix}$
			•[3] know to use scalar product equal to zero		•[3] $\overrightarrow{TB} . \overrightarrow{TC} = 0$
			•[4] start to solve		•[4] $15(c-3)+15\times(-2)+6\times(-5)=0$
			•[5] complete		•[5] (7,0,0)
2.	(a)		Ans: $x = 2$	5	
			•[1] know to differentiate		•[1] $\frac{dy}{dx}$
			•[2] differentiate		•[2] $\frac{dy}{dx} = 12x - 3x^2$
			•[3] set derivative equal to 12		•[3] $12x - 3x^2 = 12$
			•[4] express quadratic in standard form		•[4] $3x^2 - 12x + 12 = 0$
			•[5] solve		•[5] $x = 2$
	(b)		**Ans:** $12x - y = 8$	2	
			•[1] find y coordinate		•[1] 16
			•[2] find equation of line		•[2] $y - 16 = 12(x - 2)$
3.			Ans: proof	4	
			•[1] use discriminant		•[1] $b^2 - 4ac$ and $a = 2, b = p$ and $c = -3$
			•[2] simplify		•[2] $p^2 + 24$
			•[3] interpret discriminant		•[3] $p^2 + 24 \geq 24$ since $p^2 \geq 0$
			•[4] communicate conclusion		•[4] $b^2 - 4ac > 0 \Rightarrow$ roots are real for all values of p

Question	Marking scheme. Give one mark for each •	Max mark	Illustration of evidence for awarding a mark at each •
4. (a)	Ans: $x - 3y = -8$ •¹ find midpoint of PQ •² find gradient of PQ •³ find perpendicular gradient •⁴ state equation of perpendicular bisector	4	•¹ $(1, 3)$ •² -3 •³ $\dfrac{1}{3}$ •⁴ $y - 3 = \dfrac{1}{3}(x - 1)$
(b)	Ans: $3x + y = 1$ •¹ use parallel gradients •² state equation of line	2	•¹ -3 •² $y - (-2) = -3(x - 1)$
(c)	Ans: $\left(-\dfrac{1}{2}, \dfrac{5}{2}\right)$ •¹ use valid approach •² solve for one variable •³ state point of intersection	3	•¹ e.g. $x - 3y = -8$ $\quad\quad 9x + 3y = 3$ •² $x = -\dfrac{1}{2}$ or $y = \dfrac{5}{2}$ •³ $\left(-\dfrac{1}{2}, \dfrac{5}{2}\right)$
(d)	Ans: $\sqrt{\dfrac{5}{2}}$ •¹ identify appropriate points •² calculate distance	2	•¹ $(1, 3)$ and $\left(-\dfrac{1}{2}, \dfrac{5}{2}\right)$ •² $\sqrt{\dfrac{5}{2}}$ or $\dfrac{\sqrt{10}}{2}$ or $\sqrt{2 \cdot 5}$
5. (a)	Ans: $(-4, -2)$, $\sqrt{58}$ •¹ state coordinates of centre •² calculate radius	2	•¹ $(-4, -2)$ •² $\sqrt{58}$
(b)	Ans: proof •¹ find centre and radius of second circle •² find distance between centres of circles •³ find sum of radii of circles •⁴ communicate conclusion	4	•¹ $(4, 6)$, $\sqrt{26}$ •² $C_1C_2 = \sqrt{128} \approx 11 \cdot 3$ •³ $r_1 + r_2 = \sqrt{58} + \sqrt{26} \approx 12 \cdot 7$ •⁴ $C_1C_2 < r_1 + r_2 \Rightarrow$ circles intersect

Question			Marking scheme. Give one mark for each •	Max mark	Illustration of evidence for awarding a mark at each •
	(c)		Ans: $(-1,5),(3,1)$	5	
			•^{1} substitute		•^{1} $x^2+(4-x)^2+8x+4(4-x)-38=0$
			•^{2} express in standard form		•^{2} $2x^2-4x-6=0$
			•^{3} factorise		•^{3} $2(x+1)(x-3)=0$
			•^{4} solve for x		•^{4} $x=-1, x=3$
			•^{5} state coordinates		•^{5} $(-1,5),(3,1)$
6.			Ans: $\dfrac{\pi}{4},\dfrac{\pi}{2},\dfrac{5\pi}{4},\dfrac{3\pi}{2},$	6	
			•^{1} use double angle formula		•^{1} $2\sin x\cos x=2\cos^2 x$
			•^{2} form correct equation		•^{2} $2\sin x\cos x=2\cos^2 x=0$
			•^{3} take out common factor		•^{3} $2\cos x(\sin x-\cos x)=0$
			•^{4} proceed to solve		•^{4} $\cos x=0, \sin x=\cos x$
			•^{5} find solutions		•^{5} $\dfrac{\pi}{2}$ & $\dfrac{3\pi}{2}$
			•^{6} find remaining solutions		•^{6} $\dfrac{\pi}{4}$ & $\dfrac{5\pi}{4}$
7.			Ans: The claim is true. The wood is over 1000 years old. It contains 88% of the amount of carbon in a living tree so it is 1031 years old.	5	
			•^{1} interpret equation		•^{1} $0\cdot 88A_0=A_0 e^{-0\cdot 000124t}$
			•^{2} process equation		•^{2} $e^{-0\cdot 000124t}=0\cdot 88$
			•^{3} take log to base e		•^{3} $-0\cdot 000124t=\ln 0\cdot 88$
			•^{4} process for t		•^{4} $t=\dfrac{\ln 0\cdot 88}{-0\cdot 000124}=1031$
			•^{5} communicate conclusion		•^{5} The claim is true. The wood is over 1000 years old. It contains 88% of the amount of carbon in a living tree so it is 1031 years old.

Question			Marking scheme. Give one mark for each •	Max mark	Illustration of evidence for awarding a mark at each •
8.	(a)		Ans: proof	3	
			Method 1		**Method 1**
			$\bullet^1$ use similar triangles		$\bullet^1$
			$\bullet^2$ state ratio of corresponding sides		$\bullet^2$ $\dfrac{QR}{3-t} = \dfrac{6}{3}$
			$\bullet^3$ show steps leading to given formula for QR		$\bullet^3$ $QR = \dfrac{6}{3}(3-t)$ $= 6-2t$
			Method 2		**Method 2**
			$\bullet^1$ use equation of straight line		$\bullet^1$ $y = -2x+6$
			$\bullet^2$ substitute $QR = y$ -coordinate of Q		$\bullet^2$ $QR = -2x+6$
			$\bullet^3$ substitute x -coordinate of Q=t and show steps leading to given formula for QR		$\bullet^3$ $QR = -2t+6$ $= 6-2t$
	(b)		Ans: $x = (1.5, 3)$	6	
			$\bullet^1$ state formula for area of rectangle		$\bullet^1$ $A = t(6-2t)$
			$\bullet^2$ prepare for differentiation		$\bullet^2$ $A = 6t - 2t^2$
			$\bullet^3$ differentiate		$\bullet^3$ $\dfrac{dA}{dt} = 6 - 4t$
			$\bullet^4$ set derivative equal to 0		$\bullet^4$ $6 - 4t = 0$
			$\bullet^5$ solve for valid exact value for t		$\bullet^5$ $\dfrac{3}{2}$
			$\bullet^6$ justify nature of stationary points		$\bullet^6$ $t \ ..\dfrac{3}{2}..$ $\dfrac{dA}{dt} \quad + \ 0 \ -$

Question	Marking scheme. Give one mark for each •	Max mark	Illustration of evidence for awarding a mark at each •
9.	Ans: $\dfrac{2}{3}$ m²	8	
	•¹ know how to find limits		•¹ $2x - \dfrac{1}{2}x^2 = \dfrac{3}{2}$
	•² express quadratic in standard form		•² $\dfrac{1}{2}x^2 - 2x + \dfrac{3}{2} = 0$
	•³ factorise		•³ $\dfrac{1}{2}(x-1)(x-3) = 0$
	•⁴ find limits		•⁴ $x = 1, x = 3$
	•⁵ know to integrate upper − lower		•⁵ $\displaystyle\int_{1}^{3} 2x - \dfrac{1}{2}x^2 - \dfrac{3}{2}\, dx$
	•⁶ integrate		•⁶ $\left[x^2 - \dfrac{1}{6}x^3 - \dfrac{3x}{2} \right]_{1}^{3}$
	•⁷ substitute in limits		•⁷ $\left(3^2 - \dfrac{1}{6}\times 3^3 - \dfrac{3}{2}\times 3 \right) - \left(1^2 - \dfrac{1}{6}\times 1^3 - \dfrac{3}{2}\times 1 \right)$
	•⁸ evaluate area		•⁸ $\dfrac{2}{3}$ m²

Acknowledgements

Hodder Gibson would like to thank the SQA for use of any past exam questions that may have been used in model papers, whether amended or in original form.